Acknowledgments

Physics in general and experimental physics in particular is a field of research where new findings are not discovered by isolated individuals but rather by teams. This work is no exception being the result of numberless discussions, cooperations, suggestions and technical assistances.

First and foremost I would like to thank Cornelia Denz, my boss and supervisor of this thesis, for establishing and maintaining an extraordinarily creative, scientifically fruitful and in all facets pleasant working atmosphere in her research group. Above all, however, I thank her for not seeing me as a student but rather as a scientist. She strongly supported me in presenting my results at various international conferences, making multiple external research visits, participating in numberless project meetings, contributing my ideas to different project proposals, and managing own projects self-dependently—from the initial idea to the final publications. Thank you very much!

I thank Berenike Maier for kindly serving as the second supervisor but mainly for her open-mindedness about new ideas and her critical and always very constructive opinion. Thank you very much for the absolutely uncomplicated collaboration and for several enlightening discussions.

I am deeply grateful to Christina Alpmann, Konrad Berghoff and Florian Hörner whom I had the pleasure to guide during their research activities for their theses and who constituted the most continuous and most essential participants of our optical tweezers team. Only by working as a team were we able to promote the field of optical micromanipulation so comprehensively in this short time. I thank you so much for your outstanding motivation, your pleasure to perform even most complex research tasks and to discuss even the most fantastic ideas and, most of all, for the very successful cooperation in our jointly accomplished projects.

Special thanks go to Michael Eßeling, Christina Heßeling, Frank Holtmann, Wolfgang Horn, Jörg Imbrock, Björn Kemper, Alvin Sashala Naik, Lena Dewenter, Álvaro Barroso Peña, André Devaux, Stefan Gläsener, and Manoel Veiga Gutierrez with whom I had the pleasure to collaborate in smaller and bigger projects that did not directly find the way into this thesis but helped to open my mind and look at my research from different perspectives.

Many thanks go to Christian Mertens for the excellent and reliable aid with technical issues, Diana Nordhaus for her help with many administrative issues, and the employees of the electronics and mechanics workshops for the usually quick and always professional implementation of even unusual wishes.

Thank you very much, Peter Noçon, for proof-reading the original manuscript and for the very helpful hints concerning the English language.

Most of all, however, I wish to thank my wife Tanja, my son Justus as well as Justus' grandparents. Thank you so much for making the exciting but also risky experiment "doctorate, job and family" such a success!

Münster, February 2012   Mike Woerdemann

Contents

Chapter 1
Motivation and Outline

Optical tweezers, laser tweezers, optical (micro) manipulation, or optical trapping are but the most common words for a class of methods that has developed to a huge range of applications in, and novel insights into, such divergent fields as e.g. theoretical thermodynamics on the one hand, and biomedicine on the other. The basic idea is simple end elegant: Light with high intensity transfers some of its momentum to a small particle and by this means exerts a force on the particle. This provides an in most aspects unique way to handle nano- and microscopic objects, ranging from simple plastic spheres to highly complex biological cells, without any kind of physical contact and on length scales that cannot easily be accessed by any other technique.

It was as early as 1970 that Arthur Ashkin demonstrated that focused laser light is intense enough and that microscopic particles have a sufficiently small mass so that they can be accelerated and trapped solely by its radiation pressure (Ashkin 1970). While the pioneering researchers probably were mainly driven by their curiosity, soon there were ideas about how the enormous potential of the new method could be used for essential scientific questions, usually accompanied by a further development of the basic method according to the specific needs. A complete list of only the most important developments, branches and technical milestones would be too long, but two selected examples can provide an idea of the eventful history of optical trapping and manipulation. The insight that a tightly focused laser beam cannot only accelerate but also confine a microscopic particle three-dimensionally without the need of any further forces led to a concept that was originally named "single-beam gradient force optical trap" and is nowadays widely know as "optical tweezers" (Ashkin et al. 1986). This particular implementation of an optical trap has the advantage that it can easily be integrated into a standard laboratory microscope—certainly one reason for its popularity in biological laboratories, where it is meanwhile commonly used to measure extremely small forces. Another important achievement was the first optical confinement of single atoms, when Steven Chu and his colleagues combined an optical trap in a very clever way with a suitable cooling method for the atoms

M. Woerdemann, *Structured Light Fields*, Springer Theses,
DOI: 10.1007/978-3-642-29323-8_1, © Springer-Verlag Berlin Heidelberg 2012

(Chu et al. 1986). This work finally led to the 1997 Nobel prize "for development of methods to cool and trap atoms with laser light". [1]

After many other innovations, it was only in the year 2000 that it was realised that holographic beam-shaping can be of use for the extension of optical tweezers. With computer-generated diffractive optical elements—or holograms—it became possible to structure the wavefront of a laser beam in such a way that it was able to simultaneously confine multiple microscopic particles (Dufresne et al. 2001). The final breakthrough of "holographic optical tweezers", however, needed two more years when liquid crystal micro displays were first utilised to structure a wavefront dynamically, without the need for time-consuming hologram development (Curtis et al. 2002). Together with the competing technology of time-shared traps (Sasaki et al. 1991), holographic optical tweezers can be considered as the method of choice for the majority of applications where a multitude of particles are supposed to be controlled simultaneously. If full three-dimensional control of multiple particles is desired or if objects with a non-spherical shape need to be aligned and oriented, holographic optical tweezers are unrivalled (Hörner et al. 2010).

Although optical tweezers and, in particular, holographic optical tweezers are very successful in various fields of science, they are subject to fundamental limitations which will be discussed comprehensively in Chap. 2. The main objective of this thesis is the development and experimental investigation of novel schemes for optical control of matter that address current limitations of the established techniques. These schemes are summarised as *structured light fields* as they rely on the spatial and/or temporal tailoring of a light field's intensity and phase.

Chapter 3 suggests the novel scheme of *holographic phase contrast* to generate multiple, dynamic optical traps utilising the flexibility of a computer-controlled spatial light modulator but without the need to calculate Fourier holograms (Woerdemann et al. 2009). After a discussion of the advantages of non-Fourier-plane methods in general, a brief review of optical volume holography in photorefractive crystals is provided, as this is the basic principle employed for the phase-to-intensity transfer. The principle of holographic phase contrast is proven experimentally and the performance of the scheme is discussed.

In Chap. 4 , the potential of counter-propagating geometries for optical trapping is explored. Counter-propagating implementations of optical traps can have many advantages like higher working distance, larger freedom of movement along the beam axis, or lower peak intensities, but they require a more complex optical and mechanical system. Optical phase-conjugation can be used to automatically generate a back-propagating wave that matches any incident light field. After a concise description of optical phase-conjugation, it is shown experimentally that phase-conjugation can be utilised for a powerful implementation of counter-propagating optical traps. It is demonstrated that not only single counter-propagating optical traps can be achieved with optical phase-conjugation, but light fields arbitrarily structured in space and time can be reversed (Woerdemann et al. 2010b).

---

[1] http://www.nobelprize.org/—the official website of the nobel prize, Sept 2011.

Chapter 5 introduces the class of *non-diffracting* beams and discusses their application for optical moulding of matter. Non-diffracting beams feature a significantly increased Rayleigh length and thus are suitable for optical potentials that are extended along the beam axis. Mathieu beams as an example for complex non-diffracting beams are investigated and novel schemes for optical trapping are suggested and demonstrated experimentally (Alpmann et al. 2010).

In Chap. 6 the widely unknown class of *Ince-Gaussian* beams is reviewed and their applicability to optical trapping is investigated. Ince-Gaussian beams are a general solution of the paraxial Helmholtz equation and contain Hermite-Gaussian and Laguerre-Gaussian modes as limiting cases. They hence share many exciting properties like the ability to transfer optical orbital angular momentum or their self-similarity with light modes already established for optical trapping and feature an unmatched diversity in available intensity patterns. Applications in optical organisation of microparticles are demonstrated experimentally (Woerdemann et al. 2011).

Advanced applications of holographic optical tweezers are shown in Chap. 7. After a short review of the basic concepts and some established applications, two new applications are explored. First, the full three-dimensional position and orientation control of rod-shaped bacteria is demonstrated with a multi-trap approach (Hörner et al. 2010). Then, the developed scheme for full optical control on non-spherical objects is utilised for optical control and organisation of cylindrical microporous nano-containers (Woerdemann et al. 2010c). This leads to a novel method for achieving *hierarchical supramolecular organisation* with a hitherto unknown selectivity and precision (Woerdemann et al. 2010a).

The thesis concludes with a summary of the results presented and gives an outlook on further investigations that are beyond the scope of this thesis.

References

Alpmann C, Bowman R, Woerdemann M, Padgett M, Denz C (2010) Mathieu beams as versatile light moulds for 3D micro particle assemblies. Opt Express 18:26084–26091

Ashkin A (1970) Acceleration and trapping of particles by radiation pressure. Phys Rev Lett 24:156–159

Ashkin A, Dziedzic J, Bjorkholm J, Chu S (1986) Observation of a single-beam gradient force optical trap for dielectric particles. Opt Lett 11:288–290

Chu S, Bjorkholm J, Ashkin A, Cable A (1986) Experimental observation of optically trapped atoms. Phys Rev Lett 57:314–317

Curtis J, Koss B, Grier D (2002) Dynamic holographic optical tweezers. Opt Commun 207:169–175

Dufresne E, Spalding G, Dearing M, Sheets S, Grier D (2001) Computer-generated holographic optical tweezer arrays. Rev Sci Instrum 72:1810–1816

Hörner F, Woerdemann M, Müller S, Maier B, Denz C (2010) Full 3D translational and rotational optical control of multiple rod-shaped bacteria. J Biophotonics 3:468–475

Sasaki K, Koshioka M, Misawa H, Kitamura N, Masuhara H (1991) Pattern-formation and flow-control of fine particles by laser-scanning micromanipulation. Opt Lett 16:1463–1465

Woerdemann M, Holtmann F, Denz C (2009) Holographic phase contrast for dynamic multiple-beam optical tweezers. J Opt A: Pure Appl Opt 11:034010

Woerdemann M, Alpmann C, Hoerner F, Devaux A, De Cola L, Denz C (2010a) Optical control and dynamic patterning of zeolites. SPIE Proc 7762:77622E

Woerdemann M, Berghoff K, Denz C (2010b) Dynamic multiple-beam counter-propagating optical traps using optical phase-conjugation. Opt Express 18:22348–22357

Woerdemann M, Gläsener S, Hörner F, Devaux A, De Cola L, Denz C (2010c) Dynamic and reversible organization of zeolite L crystals induced by holographic optical tweezers. Adv Mater 22:4176–4179

Woerdemann M, Alpmann C, Denz C (2011) Optical assembly of microparticles into highly ordered structures using Ince-Gaussian beams. Appl Phys Lett 98:111101

Chapter 2
Introduction to Optical Trapping

Light that is reflected, refracted or absorbed by small particles in general undergoes a change in momentum. In turn, the particles experience an analogous change in momentum, i.e. a resulting force. It was demonstrated already more than 40 years ago that radiation pressure from a (laser) light source can accelerate microscopic particles (Ashkin 1970). The historically most important insight, however, was that microscopic particles cannot only be pushed by the radiation pressure, but they can be at will confined in all three dimensions, leading to the powerful concept of optical tweezers (Ashkin et al. 1986).

This chapter provides a short overview on the basic physical principles and concepts of optical trapping and reviews important milestones. While the focus of this overview will be on classical optical tweezers, related concepts and applications are discussed when beneficial for the understanding of the following chapters.

2.1 A Short Note on the History

Although it contradicts everyday experience, it has been accepted ever since the emergence of the electromagnetic theory by Maxwell that light waves are associated with linear momentum (Maxwell 1873). The theoretical treatment consistently substantiates early explanations by Kepler, who believed that the repulsive forces of the sun on comet tails issued from the radiation pressure of the sun light (Lebedev 1901). Even before the invention of lasers, observations with elaborate experimental apparatus proved the existence of radiation pressure qualitatively (Lebedev 1901; Nichols and Hull 1901) and quantitatively (Nichols and Hull 1903). Optical micromanipulation as a means to selectively confine and move small particles, however, requires very high intensity gradients that are only possible with laser light sources. This field of activities was initiated roughly 40 years ago by Ashkin in his seminal paper on "acceleration and trapping of particles by radiation pressure" (Ashkin 1970), who used a weakly focused laser beam in order to guide particles. He not only observed the acceleration of microscopic particles by the radiation force but also noticed a

M. Woerdemann, *Structured Light Fields*, Springer Theses,
DOI: 10.1007/978-3-642-29323-8_2, © Springer-Verlag Berlin Heidelberg 2012

gradient force, pulling transparent particles with an index of refraction higher than the surroundings towards the beam axis. Furthermore, he proposed and demonstrated the concept of counter-propagating optical trapping (cf. also Chap. 4), where the opposed radiation pressure of two laser beams leads to the stable three-dimensional confinement of particles. Soon, other stable optical traps were demonstrated, including the optical levitation trap where gravitational forces counteract the radiation pressure (Ashkin and Dziedzic 1971). A major breakthrough in the field of optical micromanipulation was the demonstration of a "single beam gradient force trap", which is nowadays known as *optical tweezers* (Ashkin et al. 1986). In optical tweezers, a single laser beam is very tightly focused through a high numerical aperture lens and by this means can establish gradient forces counteracting the scattering forces in propagation direction. This simple and elegant implementation of an optical trap enables the stable, three-dimensional optical trapping of dielectric particles.

Based on these fundamental findings, a whole field of optical micromanipulation has developed. On the one hand, optical tweezers have been further developed towards versatile, multifunctional tools by means of time-sharing approaches, holographic beam-shaping, and an uncountable number of technological refinements. One the other hand, a wide range of alternative approaches has emerged that go beyond the concept of single or multiple discrete optical tweezers but provide optical landscapes, tailored to a specific problem. A short section at the end of this chapter gives an idea of some of these novel concepts.

2.2 Basic Physical Principles of Optical Tweezers

Optical tweezers can be qualitatively understood in terms of geometric ray optics. Consider a spherical, transparent particle in a light field that has an inhomogeneous intensity distribution in a plane transverse to the optical axis, for example a collimated Gaussian beam. Furthermore, we recall that any light ray is associated with linear momentum flux of $p = n_{\mathrm{med}} P / c$, for a ray of power P, travelling in a medium with the refractive index n_{med}. Tracing two rays that are incident symmetrically on the sphere but have different intensities, as depicted in Fig. 2.1a, it is easy to see that the vector sum of the momentum flux points away from the region of highest intensity. Consequently, the sphere will experience a reaction force along the intensity gradient, the gradient force F_{grad} (Ashkin et al. 1986). The gradient force is accompanied by the scattering force F_{scat} along the optical axis, which is further enhanced by reflection from the surfaces and absorption.

Now consider a tightly focused beam (cf. Fig. 2.1b) as is typical of optical tweezers. The spherical particle acts as a weak positive lens and changes the degree of divergence or convergence of the focused light field. If the angle of the incident rays is high enough, this can result in axial forces F_z that point backward if the particle is positioned behind the focus of the rays. By this means, a stable trapping position for the particle is achieved, i.e. any (small) displacement of the particle will result in a restoring force toward the equilibrium position (Ashkin et al. 1986; Ashkin 1992).

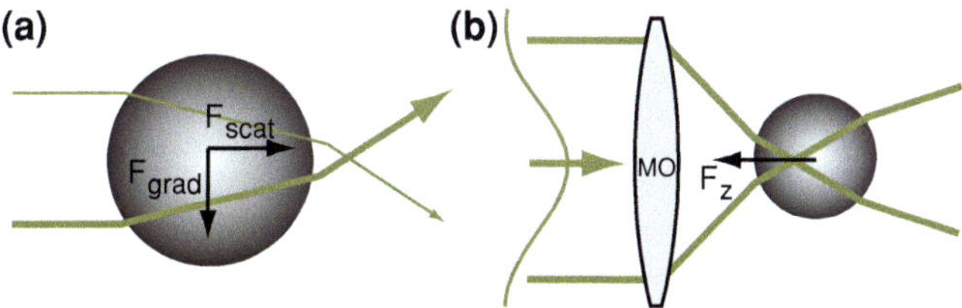

Fig. 2.1 Basic principle of optical tweezers in the geometric optics regime. **a** A transverse intensity gradient will result in a gradient force F_{grad} pointing towards the region of highest intensity. **b** Strong focusing through a microscope objective (*MO*) can result in a backward force along the optical axis (F_z)

Geometric optics yields a good qualitative picture but can also describe optical tweezers quantitatively if the limits of the regime are respected. Naturally, geometric optics only poorly describes the light field in the vicinity of the focus and furthermore neglects any effects of diffraction and interference (Nieminen et al. 2010; Stilgoe et al. 2008). Hence, geometric optics can only describe the limiting regime of particles that are large compared to the wavelength of the light field ($d \gg \lambda$) (Ashkin 1992). For quantitatively accurate results, as a rule of thumb usually the smallest dimension of the particle should be at least 20 times the optical wavelength (Nieminen et al. 2007).

An alternative approximate description of optical tweezers is the consideration of particles that are very small compared to the wavelength ($d \ll \lambda$). In this *Rayleigh regime*, particles can be seen as infinitesimal induced point dipoles that interact with the light field. It is well known that a sphere of radius r in a homogeneous electric field $\vec{E}$ will be polarised and have an induced dipole moment of (Nieminen et al. 2007)

$$\vec{p}_{\mathrm{dipole}} = 4\pi n_{\mathrm{med}}^2 \epsilon_0 r^3 \left(\frac{m^2 - 1}{m^2 + 2} \right) \vec{E}, \tag{2.1}$$

with the relative refractive index of the particle $m = n_{\mathrm{part}}/n_{\mathrm{med}}$, and the dielectric constant in the vacuum ϵ_0. Owing to this dipole moment, the particle will experience a force in a non-uniform electric field (Harada and Asakura 1996)

$$\vec{F}_{\mathrm{grad}} = \pi n_{\mathrm{med}}^2 \epsilon_0 r^3 \left(\frac{m^2 - 1}{m^2 + 2} \right) \nabla |\vec{E}|^2. \tag{2.2}$$

For small particles, this equation is also valid for a time-varying electric field and in this case, the force can be written in terms of the intensity I of the light field:

$$\vec{F}_{\mathrm{grad}} = \frac{2\pi n_{\mathrm{med}} r^3}{c} \left(\frac{m^2 - 1}{m^2 + 2} \right) \nabla \vec{I}. \tag{2.3}$$

This force obviously depends on the gradient of the intensity and, hence, naturally is called gradient force. It points up the gradient for $m > 1$, i.e. for high-index

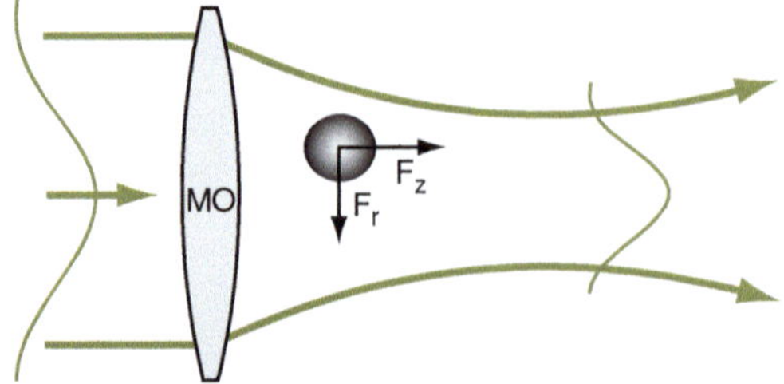

Fig. 2.2 Basic principle of optical tweezers in the Rayleigh regime. A particle exposed to a light field—a mildly focused Gaussian beam in this example—experiences a transverse force F_r and a force along the beam axis F_z

particles. For a static field, this expression would give the total force (Nieminen et al. 2007). In case of time-varying fields, the oscillating dipole can be considered as an antenna that radiates energy. The (vectorial) difference between energy removed from the incident field and energy reradiated by the particle accounts for an associated amount of change in momentum flux and hence results in a scattering force that has a magnitude of (Harada and Asakura 1996)

$$F_{\text{scat}} = \frac{8\pi n_{\text{med}}k^4 r^6}{3c} \left(\frac{m^2 - 1}{m^2 + 2}\right) I, \tag{2.4}$$

with the wavenumber $k = 2\pi/\lambda$. If the particle has absorbing properties, an additional force arises which also depends on the intensity but is proportional to r^3 rather than r^6 (Nieminen et al. 2010). The sum of these forces, including the gradient force, can be separated into a transverse component F_r and axial component F_z as depicted in Fig. 2.2.

With an increasing degree of focusing, the three-dimensional intensity gradients increase, the (axial) gradient force becomes stronger than the scattering force, and three-dimensional trapping can become possible. Comparing the scaling of the gradient force [Eq. (2.3)] and the scattering force [Eq. (2.4)] with the particle radius, one could expect that small particles below a certain threshold can always be trapped. This is not the case because there is an additional force due to the Brownian molecular motion of the particle. The thermal kinetic energy associated with the Brownian motion is $k_B T$, with the Boltzmann's constant k_B and the temperature T. This energy has to be compared to the depth of the optical trapping potential well, generated by the conservative gradient force [1]:

$$U = -\frac{2\pi n_{\text{med}} r^3}{c} \left(\frac{m^2 - 1}{m^2 + 2}\right) I + C, \tag{2.5}$$

where C is an arbitrary integration constant. Furthermore, the drag force due to the dynamic viscosity η, which is $F_{\text{drag}} = -6\pi\eta r v$ for a spherical particle with radius $r = d/2$ and velocity v, will decrease with the radius and thus less efficiently damp the Brownian motion.

---

[1] The potential energy is derived by integrating Eq. (2.3), assuming that the gradient force is conservative.

Both the geometric optical approximation and the Rayleigh approximation allow for an intuitive understanding of the physical principles of optical trapping, but their quantitative validity is restricted for typically trapped particles, which are often in the order of the optical wavelength ($d \approx \lambda$). In this intermediate regime, a more rigorous treatment based on fundamental electromagnetic theory is required for the quantitatively correct description of optical tweezers.

2.3 Optical Trapping as a Scattering Problem

In practice, many particles typically manipulated with optical tweezers, like biological cells or colloidal particles, are in the intermediate regime where the particle size is in the order of the wavelength of the trapping laser light. Furthermore, for optical tweezers the incident light field often is tightly focused to a very small focal spot, in contradiction to the paraxial approximation. Thus, the light fields need to be described rigorously in terms of the full Maxwell equation or the vectorial Helmholtz equation[2] in order to get quantitatively precise results.

In the following we will have a brief look at a rigorous description of optical tweezers that is based on the classical Lorenz-Mie theory and the closely related T-matrix method. In principle, optical trapping of homogeneous, optically linear and isotropic microspheres can be described analytically by Lorenz-Mie solutions (Mie 1908) for the scattering of the incident light at the sphere (Nieminen et al. 2007). The original Lorenz-Mie description, however, is restricted to plane-wave illumination, which obviously is not applicable to optical tweezers. The extension to arbitrary illumination is commonly called *generalised Lorenz-Mie theory* (Gouesbet 2009). Therefore, the incident light field $\vec{E}_{\text{inc}}$ and the scattered light field $\vec{E}_{\text{scat}}$ are represented in terms of vector spherical wavefunctions (VSWFs) (Nieminen et al. 2007):

$$\vec{E}_{\text{inc}} = \sum_{n=1}^{\infty} \sum_{m=-n}^{n} a_{nm} \vec{M}_{nm}^{(3)} + b_{nm} \vec{N}_{nm}^{(3)} \tag{2.6}$$

$$\vec{E}_{\text{scat}} = \sum_{n=1}^{\infty} \sum_{m=-n}^{n} p_{nm} \vec{M}_{nm}^{(1)} + q_{nm} \vec{N}_{nm}^{(1)}. \tag{2.7}$$

Here, $\vec{M}_{nm}^{(i)}$, $\vec{N}_{nm}^{(i)}$ are the VSWFs of the ith type, n, m are the radial and azimuthal mode indices, and a_{nm}, b_{nm}, p_{nm}, q_{nm} are the expansion coefficients. The choice of VSWFs as the basis for the incident and scattered light field is convenient with respect to the generalised Lorenz-Mie theory (Nieminen et al. 2003). The expansion coefficients usually cannot be found analytically for beams typically used in

---

[2] We recall that solutions of the Helmholtz equation are solutions of the Maxwell equations if we additionally require that the fields are divergence free, i.e. $\nabla \cdot \vec{E} = 0$ and $\nabla \cdot \vec{H} = 0$ (Novotny and Hecht 2006)

optical tweezers, like the fundamental Gaussian beam or Laguerre-Gaussian beams, but usually are derived numerically because these beams are not exact solutions of the vectorial Helmholtz equation but only solve the paraxial Helmholtz equation (Nieminen et al. 2003). One method is using a least-square fit to produce a representation of the incident light field that matches the (paraxial) beam in the far field (Nieminen et al. 2007; Nieminen et al. 2003). Once the incident light field is given in the representation of Eq. (2.6), the task to solve is finding the p_{nm}, q_{nm} of the light field that has been scattered by the particle. When incident and scattered light fields are known, there are straightforward means of calculating the force and torque acting on the particle by considering the (angular) momentum content of the incident and scattered light (Nieminen et al. 2007).

For the case of a homogeneous, isotropic sphere there is no coupling between different modes and, thus, the scattered and incident fields are connected by

$$p_{nm} = a_n a_{nm} \tag{2.8}$$

$$q_{nm} = b_n b_{nm}, \tag{2.9}$$

with the coefficients a_n, b_n given by the Lorenz-Mie theory (Nieminen et al. 2007). In the more general case of an arbitrarily shaped particle, coupling needs to be considered and the expansion coefficients of the scattered wave are given by (Nieminen et al. 2007)

$$p_{n'm'} = \sum_{n=1}^{n_{\max}} \sum_{m=-n}^{n} A_{n'm'nm} a_{nm} + B_{n'm'nm} b_{nm} \tag{2.10}$$

$$q_{n'm'} = \sum_{n=1}^{n_{\max}} \sum_{m=-n}^{n} C_{n'm'nm} a_{nm} + D_{n'm'nm} b_{nm}, \tag{2.11}$$

where the infinite sums have been truncated at $n_{\max}$. With the convention that the coefficients $p_{n'm'}$, $q_{n'm'}$ are elements of the column vector $\vec{p}$ and a_{nm}, b_{nm} are represented by $\vec{a}$, we can write

$$\vec{p} = \mathbf{T}\vec{a}, \tag{2.12}$$

with the transition matrix $\mathbf{T}$, which often simply is called *T-matrix*. For the case of spherical particles, this matrix is diagonal and completely determined by the Mie coefficients. While the matrix is more complex for a general particle, however, it still only depends on the properties of the particle and is independent of the light field. This particular property is important for the numerical calculation for optical tweezers when the trapping forces or torques at (many) different positions in the light field are of interest or when different light fields are considered. In these cases, the T-matrix only needs to be calculated once for a given particle and can be reused for further calculations, dramatically decreasing calculation times especially for non-spherical particles.

Figure 2.3 shows a few examples of numerical simulations for different numerical apertures of the focusing lens. The numerical code used for these simulations is founded on a publicly available Matlab computational toolbox (Nieminen et al. 2007) and was extended in order to calculate two-dimensional intensity profiles and the full three-dimensional force field. In Fig. 2.3a it can be seen that a Gaussian beam which is focused by a lens with a numerical aperture of $NA = 0.75$ does not create a stable potential well for the particle. Increasing the numerical aperture to $NA = 1.0$ (Fig. 2.3b) yields an equilibrium position for the simulated particle of a diameter of one wavelength and a relative refractive index of $n_{rel} = n_{part}/n_{med} \approx 1.19$. However, this potential minimum is rather shallow and only even stronger focusing (e.g. $NA = 1.34$, Fig. 2.3c) can create a potential well deep enough to trap the particle in the presence of Brownian motion. For all cases it can be seen that the trapping potential is weakest in direction of beam propagation $(+z)$ because the scattering force always has a component pointing in this direction which only can be compensated by the gradient force in $-z$ direction.

2.4 The Paraxial Approximation

A rigorous treatment of optical tweezers within electromagnetic theory is obviously the favourable approach to obtain a quantitative description of the local forces acting on arbitrary particles. On the other hand, the approximate descriptions derived in Sect. 2.2 proved to be very useful for understanding the physical origin of the optical potential well. In particular, Eq. (2.5) for the optical energy potential due to the gradient force in the Rayleigh regime is valid—assuming the small-particle approximation holds true—for any three-dimensional light intensity distribution $I(\vec{r})$. In the following, we will see that an adequate estimate of the quality of the optical potential landscape can be obtained even when paraxial beams are assumed—an assumption which obviously needs to be carefully discussed in the regime of tightly focused laser beams.

A useful measure for evaluating the validity of the paraxial approximation is the ratio of wavelength λ and beam waist ω_0 (Davis 1979)

$$s = \frac{\lambda}{2\pi\omega_0}, \tag{2.13}$$

which should be small for paraxial beams. Tight focusing narrows the beam waist and thus increases the errors introduced by the paraxial approximation. In order to get an impression of the quantity of the errors, we assume a fundamental Gaussian beam which is focused through a microscope objective lens with a numerical aperture of $NA = 1.1$. With the definition of the numerical aperture $NA = n_{med} \sin(\Theta)$ and the beam waist of $\omega_0 = \lambda/(\pi\Theta)$ (Eichler et al. 2004) and a typical value of the refractive index of the immersion oil $n_{med} = 1.52$, the parameter s can be

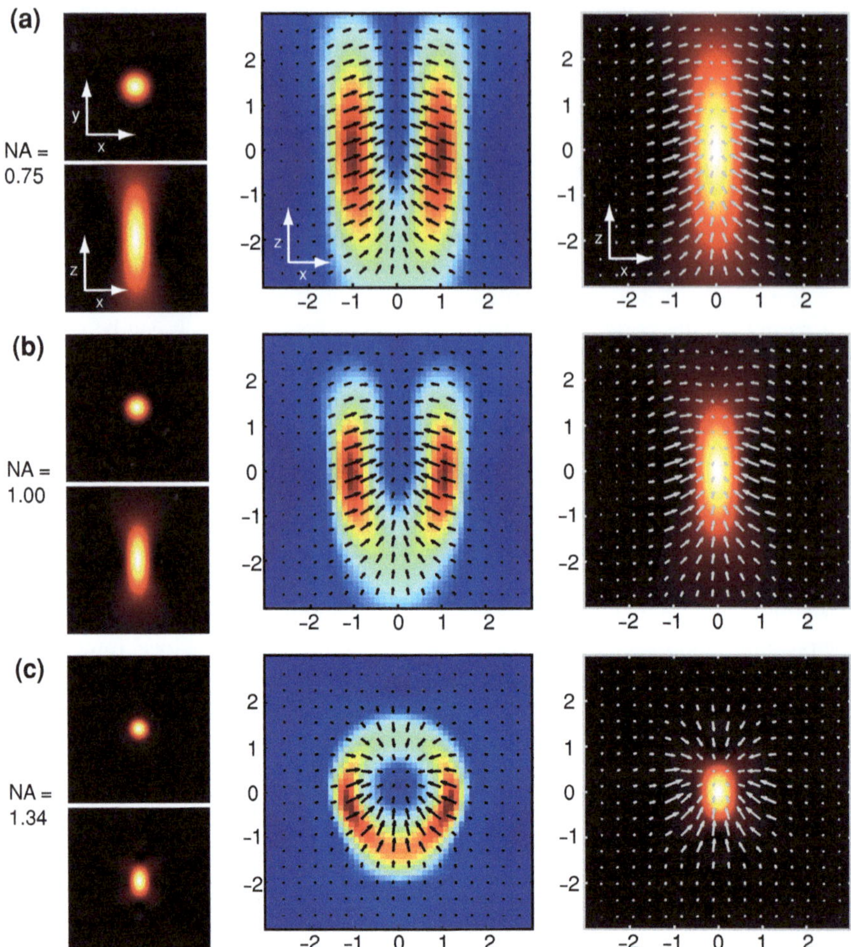

Fig. 2.3 Optical potential landscape for a spherical particle due to a focused fundamental Gaussian beam propagating in $+z$ direction. Three different numerical apertures for the focusing lens are considered (**a**)–(**c**). In the left column, transverse and longitudinal intensity distributions of the focused light fields are shown. The displayed area is about 3×3 wavelengths. In the middle column, the numerically calculated local forces acting on the particle are shown (*arrow matrix*). The absolute values are additionally encoded in the colour values behind the *arrow matrix*, emphasising areas of low (*blue*) and high (*red*) forces. In the *right* column, the same force field is displayed upon the intensity distribution, showing the shift between focus position and equilibrium position of the particle. All axes are labelled in units of wavelength. The particle is assumed to have a diameter of one wavelength and a refractive index of $n_{\mathrm{particle}} = 1.59$; the surrounding fluid is assumed to have a refractive index of $n_{\mathrm{med}} = 1.34$ (water)

calculated as[3] $s \approx 0.4$. For this regime, following Barton and Alexander (Barton and Alexander 1989), an average deviation of the electric field of approximately 20% from the rigorous treatment can be expected. Although this is a large error, and the maximal error can be even more significant in particular locations in the vicnity of the focus, it can be expected that the qualitative structure of the field is adequately described. In order to increase the accuracy, higher order terms can be included. For the same value $s \approx 0.4$, a fifth order approximation yields an average error of only approximately 3%.

2.5 Measuring Forces

One of the unique features of optical tweezers is their ability not only to transfer extremely small forces to micro- and nanoscopic particles but also to measure forces in the piconewton range with high precision. Although, in principle, the optical potential is known from the intensity distribution in the sample [cf. Eq. (2.5)] (Viana et al. 2007), the usual way is to probe the potential with a particle of the same kind as is to be used for the force measurement. This automatically eliminates a couple of experimental uncertainties, such as transmission properties of the microscope objective, the exact transverse beam profile, or effects due to the small-particle approximation, and includes them in the calibration. For the calibration, a particle is trapped in the optical potential well and its motion due to the Brownian molecular motion is monitored. As illustrated in Fig. 2.4a, the particle automatically scans or "explores" the shape of the potential well, having a higher probability of presence at the minimum of the potential well. Figure 2.4b shows the number $N(x)$ that a particle was observed at a particular position x, which gives the probability function $p(x)$. Often, an optical potential induced by optical tweezers can be approximated as harmonic (cf. Fig. 2.4c). In that case the calibration procedure yields a scalar calibration factor k, the stiffness of the optical trap. In this approximation, the force a particle feels is directly proportional to its displacement Δx from the equilibrium position ($x = 0$), i.e. $|\vec{F}| = k\Delta x$. Force measurement in this configuration means measuring the new equilibrium position and thus Δx as illustrated in Fig. 2.4d. As the displaced particle still underlies Brownian motion, the measured force always is a superposition of external forces and forces duc to Brownian motion. The uncertainty due to Brownian motions decreases with measurement time as the mean value of the stochastic process is exactly the (displaced) equilibrium position.

---

[3] Note that the s parameter is independent of the wavelength.

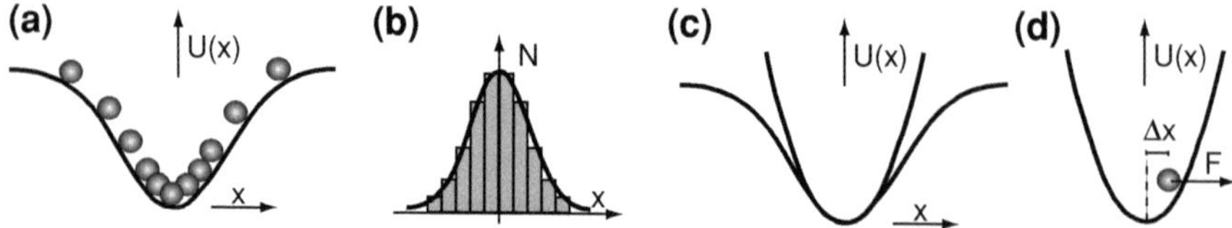

Fig. 2.4 Basic principles of force measurement. A trapped particle has a higher probability of presence at the potential minimum (**a**), resulting in an according histogram of positions (**b**). For typical configurations and applications, the potential well can be approximated as harmonic (**c**), resulting in a linear relation between external forces acting on the particle and the particle's displacement (**d**)

2.5.1 Particle Position Detection

All methods for the calibration of optical trapping potentials rely on the position tracking of a probe particle. Two methods have established for particle tracking in optical tweezers. The (lateral) particle position can be detected by observing the laser light transmitted through the particle or reflected from it. The interference pattern, e.g. of the transmitted light and the light not influenced by the particle, is detected, usually in the back focal plane of the condenser, by means of a position sensitive semiconductive sensor (Tolić-Nørrelykke et al. 2006). The sensor can be a lateral effect detector or, more frequently used, a quadrant photo diode. Tracking the intensity maximum in the back focal plane enables highly sensitive position detection of the particle. The total intensity, summed over all four quadrants of the photo diode, also gives a convenient measure of the axial position of the particle (Ghislain et al. 1994). Instead of the trapping laser, an additional laser can be used to detect the particle position.

As an alternative to photo diode based position detection, video microscopy with subsequent image analysis has gained importance with the advent of high resolution, high-speed digital video cameras in recent years (Gibson et al. 2008). While position detection with video microscopy is very flexible—e.g. it can easily be extended to multiple traps—the precision in position detection usually is lower compared to laser tracking schemes, owing to the relatively large pixel size of a typical video camera sensor. Also, the temporal resolution of video based position detection is still at least an order of magnitude lower than direct tracking of the laser beam, even with high-end video cameras.

2.5.2 Calibration Schemes

Having the position data of a trapped particle, there are several ways to characterise and calibrate the optical potential well and deduce the trap stiffness k (Neuman and Block 2004). For a harmonic potential, the overdamped oscillation of a particle in the optical trap can be described analytically and the power spectrum of the dynamics can be written as a Lorentzian distribution (Svoboda and Block 1994):

$$S(f) = \frac{k_B T}{2\pi^3 \beta \left(f_0^2 + f^2 \right)}. \tag{2.14}$$

Here, β is the viscous drag coefficient of the particle and $f_0 = k/(2\pi\beta)$ the corner frequency which can be deduced from a best fit to the power spectrum with Eq. (2.14). For a free sphere with radius r far away from any surface, the viscous drag coefficient is known to be $\beta = 6\pi\eta r$ while it has to be corrected in the vicinity of a surface by a distance-dependent factor given by Faxen's law (Svoboda and Block 1994). With a known viscous drag and the corner frequency determined from the power spectrum, the trap stiffness can be calculated. Precise calibration requires to consider further influences on the power spectrum, including frequency dependence of the drag force, effects due to the finite sampling frequency or frequency dependence of the position detection sensor (Berg-Sørensen and Flyvbjerg 2004).

The trap stiffness can also be determined by monitoring the variance of the thermal fluctuation of a trapped particle. The equipartition theorem gives the thermal kinetic energy of a particle which can be related to the optical potential energy of a trap with stiffness k (Neuman and Block 2004):

$$\frac{1}{2}k_B T = \frac{1}{2}k < x^2 >, \tag{2.15}$$

where $< x^2 >$ is the variance of the displacement from the equilibrium position. While the simplicity of this method, in particular the independence from the viscosity of the medium, is a clear advantage, it is hard to detect errors because the variance is an "intrinsically biased estimator" (Neuman and Block 2004). Since variance is derived from the square of a quantity, any noise or drift will always increase the variance and leads to an apparent decrease of the determined stiffness.

From the optical potential well, however, the probability function for the displacement of a trapped particle can be deduced (Florin et al. 1998):

$$p(x) = \exp\left(\frac{-U(x)}{k_B T}\right) = \exp\left(\frac{-kx^2}{2k_B T}\right), \tag{2.16}$$

where the first equals sign is valid for any potential $U(x)$ while the second sign holds true only for a harmonic potential.

Alternatively, the optical potential can also be probed by applying known forces and monitoring the displacement for different forces (Felgner et al. 1995). The applied force usually is viscous drag force on the particle. Consequently, all considerations on the drag force discussed above are valid. In principle it is possible to apply a discrete number of different forces or rather choose a continuous function like a sinusoidally varying force. As with the probability function, the drag force method is suitable to characterise even non-harmonic potentials. Furthermore, this method gives a straightforward way to determine the maximal force or the depth of the potential well by increasing the applied force until the particle escapes from the optical trap (Neuman and Block 2004; Malagnino et al. 2002).

In typical biological samples often particular local parameters are not directly accessible. For example, it might be difficult to determine the viscosity of the medium surrounding a trapped organelle or reference bead inside a biological cell. Furthermore, the local temperature usually is unknown as the laser focus of the optical trap induces thermal energy and heats up the sample depending on the absorption properties. A combination of the calibration schemes discussed above, however, can yield enough independent parameters to enable real-time in situ calibration even in complex biological systems (Wan et al. 2009).

2.6 Dynamic Optical Tweezers

Although single optical tweezers at a fixed position already enable many applications, it is often desirable to have a trap that can be displaced in the sample chamber. In Fig. 2.5a the basic configuration of optical tweezers is depicted. A collimated laser beam is focused through a lens with short focal length, which usually is a microscope objective, into a sample chamber that contains a fluid with dispersed particles. In order to move the focal spot and thus the optical trap to a different position in the plane orthogonal to the beam axis, the incident laser beam needs to have an angle with respect to the beam axis as shown in Fig. 2.5b. A diverging or converging beam, on the other hand, would shift the focal plane along the beam axis (Fig. 2.5c).

It is important that the beam hits the back aperture of the microscope objective always with the same diameter and at the same, centred position in order to keep the optical trap operating and its properties unchanged (Ashkin 1992; Fällman and Axner 1997). One possibility is to use an afocal telescope of two lenses in order to create an optically conjugated plane of the back aperture of the microscope objective (cf. Fig. 2.5d). Any angle introduced at this plane, e.g. by a gimbal mounted mirror (Fällman and Axner 1997), will result in a corresponding angle at the back aperture of the microscope objective without a shift in position. Similarly, any divergence introduced with a constant beam diameter at this plane, will be reproduced with a constant beam diameter at the back aperture of the microscope objective.

Position control can be automated if computer-controlled scanning mirrors are used (Sasaki et al. 1991; Misawa et al. 1992; Visscher et al. 1993). A similar approach uses acousto-optic deflectors (AODs) at the conjugate plane (Simmons et al. 1996). AODs can introduce an angle by utilising a dynamic Bragg grating inside a piezo-electric material and this function principle allows for an extremely high rate of different deflection angles to be set. One powerful application is time-shared optical tweezers, where the laser beam is directed to one position, held there for a short time and then directed to the next position. If this is done iteratively and the stopover at each position is long enough to pull back a particle to the centre position, and also the absence of the laser beam is short enough to prevent the particles escaping due

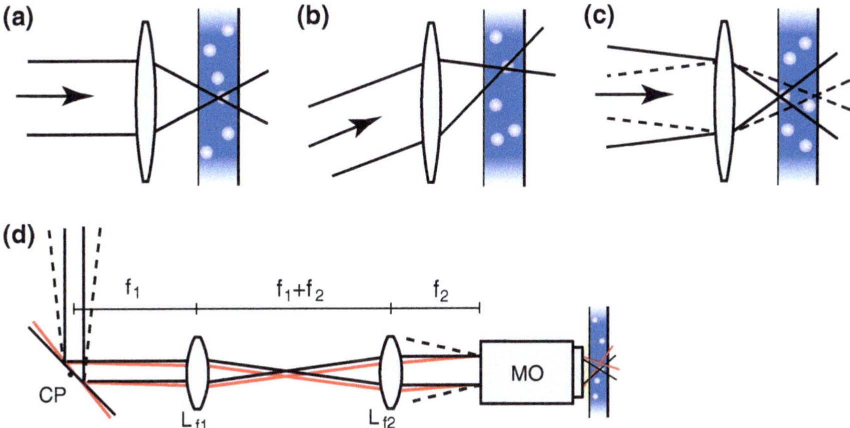

Fig. 2.5 Basic principle of position control in optical tweezers. **a–c** The position of the laser focus and hence the optical trap is translated three-dimensionally by variation of the incidence angle and divergence of the laser beam. **d** Technical realisation with a Keplarian telescope (L_{f1}, L_{f2}) and beam manipulation in a conjugate plane (*CP*) of the back aperture of a microscope objective (MO). From (Woerdemann et al. 2012)

to Brownian motion, many particles can be trapped quasi simultaneously (Sasaki et al. 1991; Visscher et al. 1993; Mio et al. 2000; Mirsaidov et al. 2008).

One ingenious way to realise control of beam angle and beam divergence in one particular plane without mechanical manipulation is diffraction at computer-generated holograms, also known as *diffractive optical elements* (DOEs) in this context. The hologram can be imprinted statically in optical materials (Dufresne and Grier 1998; Dufresne et al. 2001), e.g. by lithographic methods, or alternatively displayed by a computer-controlled spatial light modulator (SLM) (Reicherter et al. 1999; Liesener et al. 2000). The latter implementation enables versatile spatio-temporal structuring of the light field, leading to dynamic holographic optical tweezers (HOT) (Curtis et al. 2002). The classical use of HOT is the generation of multiple optical traps simultaneously. A thorough discussion of the fundamental concepts of HOT will be provided in Chap. 7.

2.7 Some Applications of Single Optical Tweezers

Optical tweezers have found a huge number of applications since their first demonstration by Arthur Ashkin and colleagues 25 years ago (Ashkin et al. 1986). In particular biological questions on a single cell or single-molecule (Svoboda and Block 1994; Stevenson et al. 2010) level can be well addressed with optical tweezers for two reasons. First, there is no other tool available that enables handling of single cells, organelles, and macromolecules with such a flexibility and precision at the same time without any physical contact that could possibly contaminate a sample. Second, optical tweezers can be used to exert defined forces and, more importantly, measure extremely small forces with an unrivalled precision (Neuman and Block 2004; Berg-Sørensen and Flyvbjerg 2004; Florin et al. 1998; Ghislain and Webb 1993; Jahnel et al. 2011).

Further applications of optical tweezers and closely related methods can be found in such diverse fields as colloidal sciences (Grier 1997), microfluidics (Leach 2006; MacDonald et al. 2003), microscopic alignment (Friese et al. 1998; O'Neil and Padgett 2002), particle separation (Imasaka et al. 1995) and sorting (MacDonald et al. 2003; Perch-Nielsen et al. 2009; Jonas and Zemanek 2008), or molecular motor dynamics (Asbury et al. 2003; Maier 2005). Optical tweezers experiments can answer fundamental physical questions, including the direct transfer of optical angular momentum (O'Neil et al. 2002; He et al. 1995), hydrodynamic interactions (Meiners and Quake 1999; Crocker 1997), and—of course—light-matter interaction (Dholakia and Zemanek 2010).

It has been demonstrated that dynamically steered and modulated optical tweezers can generate an optical thermal ratchet that biases the Brownian motion of diffusing particles (Faucheux et al. 1995). Quite recently, highly interesting insights into the physical origins of Brownian motion at very short time scales were obtained, where random diffusion is originated by ballistic motion processes (Huang et al. 2011).

This list is by no means exhaustive or complete but represents a small selection of interesting applications; an excellent overview can be found, for example, in Reference (Padgett et al. 2010).

2.8 Optical Angular Momentum and Torque

Of particular interest from the fundamental physical point of view is the ability of light fields not only to transfer linear momentum to matter but also *spin angular momentum* (SAM) and *orbital angular momentum* (OAM). SAM is strongly related to the polarisation state of light, resulting in a value of $|\vec{S}| = \pm\hbar$ per photon for circularly polarised light, where the sign is given by the chirality. An experimental proof of this relation was shown in the famous experiment by Beth (Beth 1936).

OAM is related to a tilt of the wavefront. In case of a screw wavefront dislocation with $\exp(i\ell\varphi)$ azimuthal phase dependence, also called an optical vortex, the pitch of the screw defines the topological charge ℓ. The orbital angular momentum then is given as $\ell\hbar$ per photon (Allen et al. 1992; Leach et al. 2002). A direct experimental validation of this relation was done with optical tweezers only quite recently (He et al. 1995) compared to the experimental proof of spin angular momentum.

SAM and OAM decouple in the paraxial approximation (Berry 1998; Barnett 2002) but may be transferred into each other in strongly focused beams (Nieminen et al. 2008). While spin angular momentum always is intrinsic in the sense that its value does not depend on the choice of calculation axis, OAM may be either intrinsic or extrinsic (O'Neil et al. 2002).

Low-order Laguerre-Gaussian (LG) beams are the experimentally most easily realised light fields with orbital angular momentum. Mathematically, LG beams are a complete set of free-space solutions (Okulov 2008; Saleh and Teich 2008) of the paraxial wave equation in the cylindrical system of coordinates (Saleh and Teich 2008; Dholakia and Lee 2008):

$$\text{LG}_p^\ell(\vec{r}) \propto \left(\frac{r}{\omega(z)}\right)^\ell \text{L}_p^\ell\left(\frac{2r^2}{\omega^2(z)}\right) \exp\left[\left(\frac{-r^2}{\omega^2(z)}\right) + i\left(\frac{-kr^2}{2R(z)} + (2p+\ell+1)\Phi_G(z) - \ell\varphi\right)\right]. \tag{2.17}$$

Here, z, r, φ are coordinates in the cylindrical system of coordinates, L_p^ℓ are the generalised Laguerre polynomials, p, ℓ are mode parameters and ℓ also determines the topological charge, $\omega(z)$ indicates the diameter of the beam, $R(z)$ the phase front curvature, and $\Phi_G(z)$ the Gouy phase shift.[4]

LG beams are self-similar in a sense that they maintain their transverse intensity profile during propagation except for a radial scaling factor. Of particular importance for optical trapping applications are modes with $p = 0$, which have the shape of a single ring or "doughnut". Particles are confined to this ring by transverse gradient forces and feel torque due to a transfer of OAM. In consequence, particles can move continuously on the ring of high intensity.

2.8.1 Generation of Light Fields Carrying Orbital Angular Momentum

LG beams can be generated in various ways, usually by converting other laser modes like the fundamental Gaussian TEM_{00} mode or higher modes. The *astigmatic mode converter* that consists of two cylindrical lenses with suitable distance utilises the property that any LG and Hermite-Gaussian (HG) mode can be composed of a finite number of HG modes (Allen et al. 1992; Beijersbergen et al. 1993).[5] With appropriate choice of the transverse input angle, an incident (higher order) HG mode can be decomposed in different HG modes that gain a different (Gouy) phase shift while being transmitted through the cylindrical lenses. The input HG mode and the relative phase shift between the decomposed modes can be chosen in a way that the output is a desired LG mode. The conversion efficiency of this mode converter is rather high and the mode purity can be high but it is very sensitive to the alignment and also the requirement for specific higher order HG modes is a limitation (Beijersbergen et al. 1993).

Mode conversion from a fundamental Gaussian (TEM_{00}) beam, which is readily available in high quality from the majority of commercial lasers, into an LG beam

---

[4] To keep the presentation concise, some quantities are only loosely defined here. Cf. Chap. 6, Sect. 6.1 for a more rigorous definition.

[5] More strictly speaking, LG as well as HG modes are a complete, orthogonal basis of solutions of the paraxial wave equation. Thus, any HG or LG mode can be expanded in a finite series of either modes (Beijersbergen et al. 1993).

can be achieved by imprinting the vortex phase term $\exp(i\ell\varphi)$ explicitly onto the Gaussian beam by means of a spiral phase plate (Beijersbergen et al. 1994). Depending on the overlap of input mode and desired output mode, this approach couples a majority of the input power into a desired $\mathrm{LG}^{\ell}_{p=0}$ output mode. However, still a significant part usually couples into higher p-modes, resulting in higher order rings besides the desired doughnut shape (Ando et al. 2009). The output mode purity can be significantly increased if the input beam is pre-shaped to resemble the shape of the doughnut beam before passing the spiral phase plate (Machavariani et al. 2002).

A mode converter that has not yet found wide application but is interesting from the fundamental point of view can be realised with second-harmonic generation (SHG). An LG beam that undergoes SHG results in another LG beam that does not only possess twice the frequency, but also doubles the index ℓ of the mode (Dholakia et al. 1996). By this means, higher order ℓ modes can be derived from lower order LG modes.

A very versatile approach to generate arbitrary LG modes is the use of computer-generated holograms (CGHs). In the simplest case these CGHs can be seen as a diffractive, usually off-axis, equivalent of a spiral phase plate that enables the generation of any arbitrary $\mathrm{LG}^{\ell}_{p=0}$ mode (Heckenberg et al. 1992) or $LG^{\ell=0}_{p}$ mode (Arlt et al. 1998). CGHs can be tailored for optimal efficiency or optimal purity of the produced output LG modes (Arlt et al. 1998) with remarkable results. In particular with computer-addressable SLMs, holographic mode conversion can be performed in a very flexible way. By this means, even much complexer beams that also carry OAM can be created, like higher order Bessel beams (Volke-Sepulveda et al. 2002) or helical Mathieu beams (Chavez-Cerda et al. 2002). The holographic generation of complex beams, although not with an emphasis on orbital angular momentum, will be comprehensively discussed in Chap. 5 on non-diffracting Mathieu beams and Chap. 6 on self-similar Ince-Gaussian beams. Complex superpositions of different light beams carrying OAM enable tailoring local OAM density and intensity, leading to possibly highly exciting optical landscapes (Zambrini and Barnett 2007).

2.8.2 Measurement and Applications of Optical Angular Momentum

The standard method for detecting the OAM content of a light field is to create an interferogram between the field under investigation and a reference field, usually a plane wave or TEM_{00} mode or a higher LG or HG mode (Padgett et al. 1995). The detection of the full OAM content of a arbitrary light field, however, is a non-trivial task and methods have been proposed and used to solve it under certain constraints (Parkin et al. 2006). The total SAM of a light field on the other hand is relatively easy to access by measuring the polarisation state of the light field (Parkin et al. 2006). By dynamic application of (known) SAM states, the total optical angular momentum and thus the OAM can be derived (Parkin et al. 2006; Simpson et al. 1997).

Optical angular momentum can be transferred to matter by various physical principles (Padgett and Bowman 2011). Absorption is a universal means to transfer SAM as well as OAM, i.e. absorbed photons transfer their SAM and OAM to the particle that absorbs the light. If the light is not (completely) absorbed, the difference between incident and scattered light gives the amount of transferred optical angular momentum. The SAM content of a light wave can be altered by birefringent properties of a particle. If a particle, for example, transforms (a portion of) linearly polarised incident light into circularly polarised light, the SAM of the light wave increases by $\hbar$ per photon and the particle feels the opposite amount of angular momentum in order to conserve the total amount of angular momentum. OAM an the other hand can be transferred if a particle changes the wave front tilt of the incident light wave. A microscopic version of a spiral phase plate, for example, transfers light without OAM into light carrying OAM (Asavei et al. 2009). The negative difference is transferred to the particle.

Probably the most exciting field of applications of optical angular momentum in the field of micromanipulation is the continuous driving of micro machines (Padgett and Bowman 2011; Asavei et al. 2009; Ladavac and Grier 2004). Light waves carrying optical angular momentum are also utilised in quantum optics where, e.g. the transfer of information encoded in OAM states of light (Gibson et al. 2004) is of current interest. A review of recent developments in this area can be found elsewhere (Franke-Arnold et al. 2008).

2.9 Conclusion and Perspectives

The basic concept of optical trapping has developed into many branches that partly share only the basic physical process of (angular) momentum transfer from light to matter with the original optical tweezers. In particular the sophisticated shaping of light fields has attracted many researchers in recent years and a multitude of exciting applications have arisen. The most prominent application scenario probably is the flexible creation of multiple individual spots. In Chap. 7 we will discuss holographic optical tweezers which are versatile tools enabling the dynamic generation of hundreds of individual traps simultaneously. With "generalised phase contrast", a competing technique for the generation of multiple traps has emerged (Glückstad and Palima 2009). In Chap. 3, a more advanced phase contrast method, holographic phase contrast, is introduced. A couple of higher order light modes have also been proposed and partly demonstrated for exciting applications in optical micromanipulation. In Chap. 5, for example, we will see that non-diffracting beams have many desirable features making them a promising choice for the creation of three-dimensionally structured matter. Higher order Gaussian beams and in particular the class of Ince-Gaussian beams discussed in Chap. 6 can significantly aid in applications like the organisation of microparticles, where a high degree of order is aimed at. A holographically generated array of $\mathrm{LG}^{\ell}_{p=0}$ beams was shown to be capable of creating and driving microscopic pumps that can generate a micro flow in situ (Ladavac and Grier 2004). Quite recently, it has been demonstrated that absorbing particles can be trapped in air, utilising tube-shaped (Desyatnikov et al. 2009; Shvedov et al. 2009; Shvedov et al. 2010) and bottle-shaped hollow light fields (Shvedov et al. 2010; Zhang and Chen 2011) and employing photophoretic forces (Kerker and Cooke 1982) rather than optical forces. Again, as with the examples of applications of single optical tweezers, the list of exciting innovations is endless and the mentioned works are only an arbitrary selection. Many more examples, however, will be provided within the following chapters.

References

Allen L, Beijersbergen M, Spreeuw R, Woerdman J (1992) Orbital angular momentum of light and the transformation of laguerre-gaussian laser modes. Phys Rev A 45:8185–8189

Ando T, Ohtake Y, Matsumoto N, Inoue T, Fukuchi N (2009) Mode purities of Laguerre-Gaussian beams generated via complex-amplitude modulation using phase-only spatial light modulators. Opt Lett 34:34–36

Arlt J, Dholakia K, Allen L, Padgett M (1998) The production of multiringed Laguerre-Gaussian modes by computer-generated holograms. J Mod Opt 45:1231–1237

Asavei T, Nieminen T, Heckenberg N, Rubinsztein-Dunlop H (2009) Fabrication of microstructures for optically driven micromachines using two-photon photopolymerization of UV curing resins. J Opt A: Pure Appl Opt 11:034001

Asbury C, Fehr A, Block S (2003) Kinesin moves by an asymmetric hand-over-hand mechanism. Science 302:2130–2134

Ashkin A (1970) Acceleration and trapping of particles by radiation pressure. Phys Rev Lett 24:156–159

Ashkin A (1992) Forces of a single-beam gradient laser trap on a dielectric sphere in the ray optics regime. Biophys J 61:569–582

Ashkin A, Dziedzic J (1971) Optical levitation by radiation pressure. Appl Phys Lett 19:283

Ashkin A, Dziedzic J, Bjorkholm J, Chu S (1986) Observation of a single-beam gradient force optical trap for dielectric particles. Opt Lett 11:288–290

Barnett S (2002) Optical angular-momentum flux. J Opt B: Quantum Semiclass Opt 4:S7

Barton J, Alexander D (1989) 5th-Order corrected electromagnetic-field components for a fundamental Gaussian beam. J Appl Phys 66:2800–2802

Beijersbergen M, Allen L, van der Veen H, Woerdman J (1993) Astigmatic laser mode converters and transfer of orbital angular momentum. Opt Commun 96:123–132

Beijersbergen M, Coerwinkel R, Kristensen M, Woerdman J (1994) Helical-wave-front laser-beams produced with a spiral phaseplate. Opt Commun 112:321–327

Berg-Sørensen K, Flyvbjerg H (2004) Power spectrum analysis for optical tweezers. Rev Sci Instrum 75:594–612

Berry M (1998) Paraxial beams of spinning light. In: Soskin M (ed) International conference on singular optics, vol 3487. SPIE Proceedings pp 6–11

Beth R (1936) Mechanical detection and measurement of the angular momentum of light. Phys Rev 50:115–125

Chavez-Cerda S, Padgett M, Allison I, New G, Gutierrez-Vega J, O'Neil A, MacVicar I, Courtial J (2002) Holographic generation and orbital angular momentum of high-order Mathieu beams. J Opt B: Quantum Semiclass Opt 4:S52–S57

Crocker J (1997) Measurement of the hydrodynamic corrections to the Brownian motion of two colloidal spheres. J Chem Phys 106:2837–2840

Curtis J, Koss B, Grier D (2002) Dynamic holographic optical tweezers. Opt Commun 207:169–175

Davis L (1979) Theory of electromagnetic beams. Phys Rev A 19:1177–1179

Desyatnikov A, Shvedov V, Rode A, Krolikowski W, Kivshar Y (2009) Photophoretic manipulation of absorbing aerosol particles with vortex beams: theory versus experiment. Opt Express 17:8201–8211

Dholakia K, Lee W (2008) Optical trapping takes shape: the use of structured light fields. Adv Atom Mol Opt Phys 56:261–337

Dholakia K, Zemanek P (2010) Colloquium: gripped by light: optical binding. Rev Mod Phys 82:1767

Dholakia K, Simpson N, Padgett M, Allen L (1996) Second-harmonic generation and the orbital angular momentum of light. Phys Rev A 54:R3742–R3745

Dufresne E, Grier D (1998) Optical tweezer arrays and optical substrates created with diffractive optics. Rev Sci Instrum 69:1974–1977

Dufresne E, Spalding G, Dearing M, Sheets S, Grier D (2001) Computer-generated holographic optical tweezer arrays. Rev Sci Instrum 72:1810–1816

Eichler J, Dünkel L, Eppich B (2004) Die Strahlqualität von Lasern: Wie bestimmt man Beugungs-maßzahl und Strahldurchmesser in der Praxis?

Fällman E, Axner O (1997) Design for fully steerable dual-trap optical tweezers. Appl Opt 36:2107–2113

Faucheux L, Bourdieu L, Kaplan P, Libchaber A (1995) Optical thermal ratchet. Phys Rev Lett 74:1504–1507

Felgner H, Muller O, Schliwa M (1995) Calibration of light forces in optical tweezers. Appl Opt 34:977–982

Florin E, Pralle A, Stelzer E, Horber J (1998) Photonic force microscope calibration by thermal noise analysis. Appl Phys A 66:S75–S78

Franke-Arnold S, Allen L, Padgett M (2008) Advances in optical angular momentum. Laser Photon Rev 2:299–313

Friese M, Nieminen T, Heckenberg N, Rubinsztein-Dunlop H (1998) Optical alignment and spinning of laser-trapped microscopic particles. Nature 394:348–350

Ghislain L, Webb W (1993) Scanning-force microscope based on an optical trap. Opt Lett 18:1678–1680

Ghislain L, Switz N, Webb W (1994) Measurement of small forces using an optical trap. Rev Sci Instrum 65:2762–2768

Gibson G, Courtial J, Padgett M, Vasnetsov M, Pas'ko V, Barnett S, Franke-Arnold S (2004) Free-space information transfer using light beams carrying orbital angular momentum. Opt Express, 12:5448–5456

Gibson G, Leach J, Keen S, Wright A, Padgett M (2008) Measuring the accuracy of particle position and force in optical tweezers using high-speed video microscopy. Opt Express 16:14561–14570

Glückstad J, Palima D (2009) Generalized Phase Contrast: Applications in Optics and Photonics. Springer, Netherlands

Gouesbet G (2009) Generalized Lorenz-Mie theories, the third decade: a perspective. J Quant Spectrosc Ra 110:1223–1238

Grier D (1997) Optical tweezers in colloid and interface science. Curr Opin Colloid In 2:264–270

Harada Y, Asakura T (1996) Radiation forces on a dielectric sphere in the Rayleigh scattering regime. Opt Commun 124:529–541

He H, Friese M, Heckenberg N, Rubinsztein-Dunlop H (1995) Direct observation of transfer of angular momentum to absorptive particles from a laser beam with a phase singularity. Phys Rev Lett 75:826–829

Heckenberg N, McDuff R, Smith C, White A (1992) Generation of optical phase singularities by computer-generated holograms. Opt Lett 17:221–223

Huang R, Chavez I, Taute K, Lukic B, Jeney S, Raizen M, Florin E (2011) Direct observation of the full transition from ballistic to diffusive brownian motion in a liquid. Nat Phys 7:576–580

Imasaka T, Kawabata Y, Kaneta T, Ishidzu Y (1995) Optical chromatography. Anal Chem 67:1763–1765

Jahnel M, Behrndt M, Jannasch A, Schäffer E, Grill S (2011) Measuring the complete force field of an optical trap. Opt Lett 36:1260–1262

Jonas A, Zemanek P (2008) Light at work: the use of optical forces for particle manipulation, sorting, and analysis. Electrophoresis 29:4813–4851

Kerker M, Cooke D (1982) Photophoretic force on aerosol-particles in the free-molecule regime. J Opt Soc Am 72:1267–1272

Ladavac K, Grier D (2004) Microoptomechanical pumps assembled and driven by holographic optical vortex arrays. Opt Express 12:1144–1149

Leach J (2006) An optically driven pump for microfluidics. Lab Chip 6:735–739

Leach J, Padgett M, Barnett S, Franke-Arnold S, Courtial J (2002) Measuring the orbital angular momentum of a single photon. Phys Rev Lett 88:257901

Lebedev P (1901) Untersuchungen über die Druckkräfte des Lichtes. Ann Phys 6:433

Liesener J, Reicherter M, Haist T, Tiziani H (2000) Multi-functional optical tweezers using computer-generated holograms. Opt Commun 185:77–82

MacDonald M, Spalding G, Dholakia K (2003) Microfluidic sorting in an optical lattice. Nature, 426:421–424

Machavariani G, Davidson N, Hasman E, Blit S, Ishaaya A, Friesem A (2002) Efficient conversion of a Gaussian beam to a high purity helical beam. Opt Commun 209:265–271

Maier B (2005) Using laser tweezers to measure twitching motility in neisseria. Curr Opin Microbiol 8:344–349

Malagnino N, Pesce G, Sasso A, Arimondo E (2002) Measurements of trapping efficiency and stiffness in optical tweezers. Opt Commun 214:15–24

Maxwell J (1873) A treatise on electricity and magnetism. vol 2, Clarendon Press, Oxford

Meiners J, Quake S (1999) Direct measurement of hydrodynamic cross correlations between two particles in an external potential. Phys Rev Lett 82:2211–2214

Mie G (1908) Beiträge zur Optik trüber Medien, speziell kolloidaler Metallösungen. Ann Phys 25:377–445

Mio C, Gong T, Terray A, Marr D (2000) Design of a scanning laser optical trap for multiparticle manipulation. Rev Sci Instrum 71:2196–2200

Mirsaidov U, Scrimgeour J, Timp W, Beck K, Mir M, Matsudaira P, Timp G (2008) Live cell lithography: using optical tweezers to create synthetic tissue. Lab Chip 8:2174–2181

Misawa H, Sasaki K, Koshioka M, Kitamura N, Masuhara H (1992) Multibeam laser manipulation and fixation of microparticles. Appl Phys Lett 60:310–312

Neuman K, Block S (2004) Optical trapping. Rev Sci Instrum 75:2787–2809

Nichols E, Hull G (1901) A preliminary communication on the pressure of heat and light radiation. Phys Rev (Series I) 13:307–320

Nichols E, Hull G (1903) The pressure due to radiation (second paper). Phys Rev (Series I) 17:26–50

Nieminen T, Rubinsztein-Dunlop H, Heckenberg N (2003) Multipole expansion of strongly focussed laser beams. J Quant Spectrosc Ra 79:1005–1017

Nieminen T, Knoner G, Heckenberg N, Rubinsztein-Dunlop H (2007) Physics of optical tweezers. Laser Manipulation Cells Tissues 82:207–236

Nieminen T, Loke V, Stilgoe A, Knoner G, Branczyk A, Heckenberg N, Rubinsztein-Dunlop H (2007) Optical tweezers computational toolbox. J Opt A: Pure Appl Opt 9:S196–S203

Nieminen T, Stilgoe A, Heckenberg N, Rubinsztein-Dunlop H (2008) Angular momentum of a strongly focused gaussian beam. J Opt A: Pure Appl Opt 10:115005

Nieminen T, Stilgoe A, Heckenberg N, Rubinsztein-Dunlop H (2010) Approximate and exact modeling of optical trapping. SPIE Proc 7762:77622V

Novotny L, Hecht B (2006) Principles of nano-optics. Cambridge University Press, Cambridge

Okulov A (2008) Angular momentum of photons and phase conjugation. J Phys B: At Mol Opt Phys 41:101001

O'Neil A, Padgett M (2002) Rotational control within optical tweezers by use of a rotating aperture. Opt Lett 27:743–745

O'Neil AT, MacVicar I, Allen L, Padgett MJ (2002) Intrinsic and extrinsic nature of the orbital angular momentum of a light beam. Phys Rev Lett 88:053601

Padgett M, Bowman R (2011) Tweezers with a twist. Nat Photonics 5:343–348

Padgett M, Arlt J, Simpson N, Allen L (1995) An experiment to observe the intensity and phase structure of Laguerre-Gaussian laser modes. Am J Phys 64:77–82

Padgett M, Molloy J, McGloin D, (eds) (2010) Optical tweezers: methods and applications (Series in Optics and Optoelectronics). Thaylor and Francis Group

Parkin S, Knoner G, Nieminen T, Heckenberg N, Rubinsztein-Dunlop H (2006) Measurement of the total optical angular momentum transfer in optical tweezers. Opt Express 14:6963–6970

Perch-Nielsen I, Palima D, Dam J, Glückstad J (2009) Parallel particle identification and separation for active optical sorting. J Opt A: Pure Appl Opt 11:034013

Reicherter M, Haist T, Wagemann E, Tiziani H (1999) Optical particle trapping with computer-generated holograms written on a liquid-crystaldisplay. Opt Lett 24:608–610

Saleh B, Teich M (2008) Grundlagen der Photonik. Wiley-VCH, Berlin

Sasaki K, Koshioka M, Misawa H, Kitamura N, Masuhara H (1991) Pattern-formation and flow-control of fine particles by laser-scanning micromanipulation. Opt Lett 16:1463–1465

Shvedov V, Desyatnikov A, Rode A, Krolikowski W, Kivshar Y (2009) Optical guiding of absorbing nanoclusters in air. Opt Express 17:5743–5757

Shvedov V, Rode A, Izdebskaya Y, Desyatnikov A, Krolikowski W, Kivshar Y (2010) Giant optical manipulation. Phys Rev Lett 105:118103

Shvedov V, Rode A, Izdebskaya Y, Desyatnikov A, Krolikowski W, Kivshar Y (2010) Selective trapping of multiple particles by volume speckle field. Opt Express 18:3137–3142

Simmons R, Finer J, Chu S, Spudich J (1996) Quantitative measurements of force and displacement using an optical trap. Biophys J 70:1813–1822

Simpson N, Dholakia K, Allen L, Padgett M (1997) Mechanical equivalence of spin and orbital angular momentum of light: an optical spanner. Opt Lett 22:52–54

Stevenson D, Gunn-Moore F, Dholakia K (2010) Light forces the pace: optical manipulation for biophotonics. J Biomed Opt 15:041503

Stilgoe A, Nieminen T, Knoner G, Heckenberg N, Rubinsztein-Dunlop H (2008) The effect of Mie resonances on trapping in optical tweezers. Opt Express 16:15039–15051

Svoboda K, Block SM (1994) Biological applications of optical forces. Annu Rev Biophys Biomol Struct 23:247–285

Tolić-Nørrelykke S, Schäffer E, Howard J, Pavone F, Jülicher F, Flyvbjerg H (2006) Calibration of optical tweezers with positional detection in the back focal plane. Rev Sci Instrum 77:3101–3113

Viana N, Rocha M, Mesquita O, Mazolli A, Maia Neto P, Nussenzveig H (2007) Towards absolute calibration of optical tweezers. Phys Rev E: Stat Nonlinear Soft Matter Phys 75:021914

Visscher K, Brakenhoff G, Krol J (1993) Micromanipulation by "multiple" optical traps created by a single fast scanning trap integrated with the bilateral confocal scanning laser microscope. Cytometry 14:105–114

Volke-Sepulveda K, Garces-Chavez V, Chavez-Cerda S, Arlt J, Dholakia K (2002) Orbital angular momentum of a high-order Bessel light beam. J Opt B: Quantum Semiclass Opt 4:82–89

Wan J, Huang Y, Jhiang S, Menq C (2009) Real-time in situ calibration of an optically trapped probing system. Appl Opt 48:4832–4841

Woerdemann M, Alpmann C, Denz C (2012) Three-dimensional particle control by holographic optical tweezers. In: Osten W, Reingand N (eds) Optical Imaging and Metrology. Wiley-VCH Verlag, Weinheim, to be published

Zambrini R, Barnett S (2007) Angular momentum of multimode and polarization patterns. Opt Express 15:15214–15227

Zhang P, Zhang Z, Prakash J, Huang S, Hernandez D, Salazar M, Christodoulides D, Chen Z (2011) Trapping and transporting aerosols with a single optical bottle beam generated by moiré techniques. Opt Lett 36:1491–1493

Chapter 3
Holographic Phase Contrast

Holographic optical tweezers employ diffractive optical elements (DOEs) in order to generate a multitude of optical traps. The DOE is commonly placed in a Fourier plane with respect to the plane where optical trapping occurs. An alternative to generate multiple optical traps are image-plane methods, where the structuring of the light wave is performed in a plane optically conjugate to the trapping plane. With an image-plane approach, possibly expensive computations of computer-generated holograms can be avoided completely. Furthermore, associated possible drawbacks of the diffractive approach, like losses into the zeroth diffraction order or inhomogeneous traps and ghost traps, are missing. To ensure maximal efficiency, the structuring of the light wave in the image plane is usually done with a phase-only rather than an amplitude-modulating device. A powerful way of converting a spatial phase pattern into a corresponding intensity pattern is thus an important prerequisite for efficient multiple optical traps. This chapter introduces a quantitative phase contrast technique that utilises optical volume holography and therefore is referred to as *holographic phase contrast* (HPC). After a description of the underlying concepts, HPC is demonstrated experimentally and the results and the potential for future applications in optical trapping are discussed.

3.1 Structuring Light in the Image Plane

Holographic optical tweezers (HOT) are a very versatile way to create multiple traps as will be discussed in Chap. 7. The concept of HOT relies on holographic beam-shaping with computer-calculated DOEs, which usually are positioned in a Fourier plane with respect to the trapping plane (Woerdemann et al. 2012). The hologram can be designed in such a way that in the trapping plane almost any arbitrary intensity distribution can be achieved. Multiple optical traps in this scenario are only a special case of possible complex trapping geometries. Strong optical tweezers require a high level of laser power in the trapping plane. Consequently, a high diffraction

M. Woerdemann, *Structured Light Fields*, Springer Theses,
DOI: 10.1007/978-3-642-29323-8_3, © Springer-Verlag Berlin Heidelberg 2012

efficiency is mandatory and thus usually phase-only DOEs are used. The required DOE can be produced, for example, by lithography techniques (Dufresne and Grier 1998; Dufresne et al. 2001). A far more flexible way is provided by dynamic HOT (Reicherter et al. 1999; Curtis et al. 2002), where the hologram is created by a computer-addressable (phase-only) spatial light modulator (SLM). This makes it possible to change trapping geometries without any changes in the optical setup by displaying a new hologram on the SLM. A drawback of Fourier-plane DOEs is that any local change in the trapping geometry requires the calculation of a completely new hologram. Hologram calculation time thus becomes a serious issue in real-time applications. Furthermore, Fourier holograms suffer from light that is diffracted into higher diffraction orders, in particular the zeroth order, and from ghost traps and inhomogeneities (Polin et al. 2005; Hesseling et al. 2011). Some of these issues are addressed if the hologram is not calculated as a Fourier-plane hologram but as a Fresnel hologram (Jesacher et al. 2004), and positioned accordingly in the beam path.

In principle, it is possible to simply image an amplitude mask or an amplitude SLM into the trapping plane in order to generate the desired intensity distribution. This obvious approach would eliminate the necessity of hologram calculations. However, typical trapping configurations require small areas of high intensity (the traps) and large areas of low intensity (the background). Consequently, most laser power would be absorbed by the amplitude mask or the amplitude modulator. This results in very low efficiency and requires lasers with a very high output power. Eriksen and colleagues (Eriksen et al. 2002) proposed the use of a *generalised phase contrast* method for multiple-beam optical tweezers. This approach relies on a computer-addressable phase-only SLM. The crucial point in distinction to dynamic HOT is that the SLM is not placed in a Fourier plane with respect to the trapping plane but in a conjugate image plane. In contrast to HOT, the transfer of the phase distribution on the SLM to a trapping intensity distribution thus is not done by optical Fourier transformation. Instead, a phase contrast technique (Zernike 1955) is utilised to perform this conversion. Image-plane methods in general do not require any hologram calculation but rather the desired trapping geometry is displayed directly on the SLM in the form of a corresponding phase distribution. Consequently, direct imaging methods are well suited for any real-time trapping task, with a time resolution only limited by the refresh rate of the SLM. Furthermore, the concept is not limited to multiple-beam traps, but also complex trapping geometries can be generated easily.

Besides all possible advantages, the performance of image-plane methods strongly relies on an efficient transfer of the phase distribution in the image plane into a corresponding intensity distribution in the conjugate trapping plane. The widely used approach of generalised phase contrast (Glückstad 1996) employs an optimised modification of the original Zernike phase contrast (Zernike 1955). While the concept of generalised phase contrast performs well in many scenarios (Rodrigo et al. 2005), it has limitations (Daria et al. 2003), which partly arise from the fact that it is a common path interferometer. The phase contrast relies on constructive and destructive interference of the higher spatial frequencies with the phase-shifted zeroth order, which can only be sufficiently isolated if the other spatial frequencies are high enough—

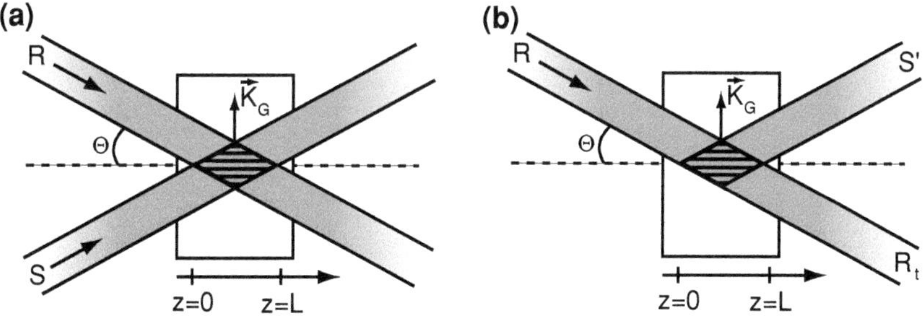

Fig. 3.1 Sketch of holographic recording (**a**), and retrieving (**b**) configuration

unavoidably resulting in halos (Zernike 1955) when the separation is imperfect. Furthermore, all light intensity unavoidably has to pass the SLM—a fact that also applies to HOT, but could be addressed with an interferometric approach featuring two separate light paths. One advantage would be that a possible bottleneck, the damage threshold of the SLM, can be widened.

Optical (volume) holography is the key to the phase-to-intensity conversion in HPC (Woerdemann et al. 2009). In the following section, the most essential fundamentals of holography in photorefractive materials are provided as necessary for a thorough discussion of the HPC concept.

3.2 Volume Holography Using the Photorefractive Effect

The basic configuration of volume holography is sketched in Fig. 3.1. For the recording of a hologram, two mutually coherent beams R, S are superimposed at an angle 2Θ inside a suitable material. At their intersection, they form a stationary interference pattern, which is transferred to a corresponding pattern in the material. The pattern contrast in the material is caused by a local change of e.g. absorbance, refractive index, or birefringence (Hariharan 1996). Once the interference pattern is recorded that way in a material it is usually referred to as *hologram*. Depending on the material utilised and the physical principle of the recording in that material, the hologram can be persistent and thus store the information on both beams for a characteristic time. After recording, the stored information is read out by one of the constituting beams which is replicated for this purpose. Let R, without loss of generality, be the beam intended for the retrieval of the recorded information. When R is incident on the hologram, it is partly diffracted by it in such a way that the diffracted part S' is proportional to the wave S and thus carries all the information that was previously encoded in S (Berger 2008).

3.2.1 Holographic Storage of a Light Wave

For a more detailed analysis we write S, R with their complex amplitudes $\hat{S}$, $\hat{R}$ as

$$S(\vec{r}) = \hat{S}e^{i\vec{k}_s\vec{r}-i\phi} \tag{3.1}$$

$$R(\vec{r}) = \hat{R}e^{i\vec{k}_r\vec{r}}, \tag{3.2}$$

with their respective wave vectors $\vec{k}_s$, $\vec{k}_r$ and a relative phase difference of ϕ. The superposition of both waves, i.e. the interference pattern within the holographic medium, can be written as[1]:

$$I(\vec{r}) = |R(\vec{r}) + S(\vec{r})|^2 \tag{3.3}$$

$$= |R(\vec{r})|^2 + |S(\vec{r})|^2 + R^*(\vec{r})S(\vec{r}) + R(\vec{r})S^*(\vec{r}) \tag{3.4}$$

$$= \hat{R}^2 + \hat{S}^2 + \hat{R}^*\hat{S}e^{-i\vec{K}_G\vec{r}-i\phi} + \hat{R}\hat{S}^*e^{i\vec{K}_G\vec{r}+i\phi}. \tag{3.5}$$

$\vec{K}_G = \vec{k}_r - \vec{k}_s$ is the grating vector of the interference pattern, whose absolute value depends on the angle 2Θ between the waves S and R and their optical wavelength λ inside the medium: $K_G(\Theta, \lambda) \equiv |\vec{K}_G| = 4\pi \sin \Theta/\lambda$.

This interference pattern is recorded in the holographic medium by a corresponding change of a material property like optical density or refractive index and the recorded pattern is known as the hologram. For the following derivation it is assumed that the material reacts on illumination with a linear variation of the refractive index, i. e. $n = n_0 + \Delta n(\vec{r})$ and $\Delta n(\vec{r}) \propto I(\vec{r})$. For a suitable holographic material this change of the refractive index is required to be persistent in a sense that it is preserved even when the writing beams S, R are no longer incident.

The stored information is retrieved by illuminating the hologram with the reference wave R initially used for recording. In a first-order approximation, the resulting waves can be written as the product of the refractive index modulation and the reference wave (Berger 2008):

$$R(\vec{r})\Delta n(\vec{r}) \propto R(\vec{r})\left(\hat{R}^2 + \hat{S}^2\right) + \hat{R}\hat{R}^*\hat{S}e^{i(\vec{k}_r-\vec{K}_G)\vec{r}-i\phi} + \hat{R}\hat{R}\hat{S}^*e^{i(\vec{k}_r+\vec{K}_G)\vec{r}+i\phi}. \tag{3.6}$$

The three terms can be identified as the transmitted part of the reference wave R, a reconstruction of the wave S, and a third wave, which is a phase-conjugate replica S^* of the wave S.

In the case of a thin hologram, all three components of the reconstructed wave can be observed. If the hologram however is a *volume hologram*, i.e. the extent in

---

[1] In order to keep the description clear effects of refraction at the interfaces of the medium and absorption inside the medium have been neglected. Neither effect affects the essence of the model and their inclusion is straightforward.

propagation direction is large compared to the fringe spacing $\Lambda = 2\pi/|\vec{K}_{\mathrm{G}}|$, the reconstructed waves also have to match the Bragg condition (Kogelnik 1969). While the Bragg condition is automatically fulfilled for R and for the reconstruction of S, it does not permit light to be diffracted into the wave S^*. Hence, the holographic readout of a volume hologram results in two waves, the non-diffracted part of the reference wave

$$R_t(\vec{r}) \propto R(\vec{r}) \left(\hat{R}^2 + \hat{S}^2\right) \propto R(\vec{r}) \tag{3.7}$$

and the part that recreates a copy S' of the wave S

$$S'(\vec{r}) \propto |\hat{R}|^2 \hat{S} e^{\mathrm{i}\vec{k}_s\vec{r}-\mathrm{i}\phi} \propto S(\vec{r}). \tag{3.8}$$

An important figure of merit is the efficiency of the diffraction at the hologram grating. It is defined as the ratio of the diffracted intensity and the incident intensity:

$$\eta = |S'|^2/|R|^2 \equiv I_{S'}/I_R \Rightarrow I_{S'} = \eta I_R. \tag{3.9}$$

In the considered case of no losses by absorption, this implies:

$$I_{R_t} \equiv |R_t|^2 = (1 - \eta)I_R, \tag{3.10}$$

stating simply that all intensity that is not diffracted into the reconstructed beam, remains in the (transmitted) reference beam. A more elaborate analysis of the diffraction at volume hologram grating follows in Sect. 3.2.3.

3.2.2 The Photorefractive Effect

One particularly versatile physical principle that allows holograms to be established in according materials is the *photorefractive effect*. It describes the light-induced change of the refractive index in photoconducting, electro-optic crystals (Ashkin et al. 1966). The transfer of a light pattern $I(\vec{r})$ into a corresponding modulation of the refractive index can be understood as a step-by-step process as depicted in Fig. 3.2a. First, the light intensity generates free charge carriers by means of photoionisation. The charge carriers are redistributed by transport processes and thus create a spatially varying electric space charge field $\vec{E}^{\mathrm{SC}}$. Finally, the linear electro-optic effect transfers the space charge field into a spatial modulation of the refractive index, which is approximately proportional to the incident light intensity pattern.

The simplest theoretical description of the photorefractive effect is given by the *band transport model* (Yeh 1993), originally developed by Kukhtarev and colleagues (Kukhtarev et al. 1979; Kukhtarev et al. 1979). Following this model, photorefractive

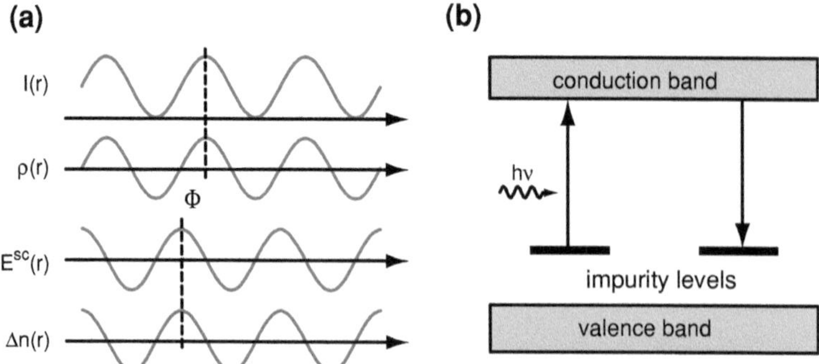

Fig. 3.2 Microscopic origin of the photorefractive effect. **a** A modulated light intensity distribution gives rise to non-homogeneous charge excitation. The electric space charge field E^{SC} due to the charge density ρ causes a corresponding modulation of the refractive index by means of the linear electro-optic effect. **b** Redistribution of charge carriers in the electronic band model

crystals possess impurities, which result in additional band gaps of the photorefractive material (cf. Fig. 3.2b). For the reason of simplicity a *one-center model* is assumed, providing donors at only one energy level with a density of N_D. Charge carriers of this intermediate energy level can be excited by photoionisation into the conduction band with a cross section s. With N_D^i being the fraction of ionised donors, the rate of electron generation is $sI\left(N_D - N_D^i\right)$,[2] proportional to the light intensity I. The rate of electrons captured by traps, i.e. ionised donors, is given as $\gamma_R N N_D^i$ with the proportionality constant γ_R and the density of electrons N. Thus, the rate equation can be written as (Yeh 1993; Kukhtarev et al. 1979):

$$\frac{\partial N_D^i}{\partial t} = sI\left(N_D - N_D^i\right) - \gamma_R N N_D^i. \tag{3.11}$$

The electrons in the conduction band are mobile and enable a current density $\vec{j}_p$, which in general consists of contributions from drift in an electric field $\vec{E}$, from a possible photovoltaic field and from diffusion:

$$\vec{j} = \vec{j}_{\text{drift}} + \vec{j}_{\text{pv}} + \vec{j}_{\text{diff}} = eN\mu_e\vec{E} + \vec{p}I + k_B T \mu_e \nabla N. \tag{3.12}$$

The mobility tensor of the electrons here is denoted as μ_e and the direction dependent material constant $\vec{p}$ quantifies the photovoltaic properties of the photorefractive material.

The principle of charge conservation requires:

$$\frac{\partial N}{\partial t} = \frac{\partial N_D^i}{\partial t} - \frac{1}{e}\nabla\vec{j}. \tag{3.13}$$

---

[2] Here we neglect thermal generation of electrons.

Finally, the electrical space charge field $\vec{E}^{\mathrm{SC}}$ that results from the redistribution of the charge carriers obeys Gauss's law

$$\epsilon\epsilon_0 \nabla \vec{E}^{\mathrm{SC}} = -e\left(N + N_A - N_D^i\right), \tag{3.14}$$

with the density of acceptors N_A which ensures charge neutrality.

Stationary refractive index grating

Equations (3.11)–(3.14)[3] describe the build-up and the properties of the electric space charge field depending on the light intensity distribution. For a stationary solution the important case of two incident, mutually coherent light waves as depicted in Fig. 3.1 is considered.

The space charge field in this particular case is given by the equation (Yeh 1993):

$$\vec{E}^{\mathrm{SC}} = -\frac{2|\hat{S}||\hat{R}|}{I_0}\tilde{E}\cos(\vec{K}_G\vec{r} - \phi - \Phi)\frac{\vec{K}_G}{|\vec{K}_G|}, \tag{3.15}$$

where, as before, $\vec{K}_G$ is the grating vector of the interference pattern. Furthermore, $I_0 = |\hat{S}|^2 + |\hat{R}|^2$ is the total intensity and $\tilde{E}$ is a proportionality constant that depends on the saturation field, the photovoltaic field, and the diffusion field (Yeh 1993). The additional phase angle Φ takes the phase shift of the space charge field and thus the refractive index grating into account. It is determined by the ratio of imaginary and real part of the complex space charge field:

$$\tan\Phi = \frac{\mathfrak{Jm}(E^{\mathrm{SC}})}{\mathfrak{Re}(E^{\mathrm{SC}})}. \tag{3.16}$$

The space charge field is transferred into a corresponding change of the refractive index n of the material by the linear electro-optic effect (Pockels' effect). In the considered case, the resulting refractive index grating is (Yeh 1993)

$$n = n_0 + \Delta n = n_0 + n_0^3 r_{\mathrm{eff}}\tilde{E}\frac{|\hat{S}||\hat{R}|}{I_0}\cos(\vec{K}\vec{r} - \phi - \Phi), \tag{3.17}$$

with n_0 being the linear refractive index of the material and Δn its modulation by the photorefractive effect. The effective electro-optic coefficient r_{eff} depends on the polarisation and the angle of incidence Θ of the involved waves and is known for the vast majority of available photorefractive materials (Yeh 1993).

Time dependence of the photorefractive effect

For the description of the photorefractive gratings so far the time dependence of the photorefractive effect has been neglected. The temporal formation of the refractive index grating is primarily determined by the finite time τ_g that is required for

---

[3] This set of equations is sometimes referred to as "Kukhtarev equations".

the space charge field to establish. A more detailed, time dependent analysis of Eqs. (3.11)–(3.14) yields a generalisation of the stationary solutions (Yeh 1993). Essentially, the conditional Eq. (3.15) for the space charge field is modified by an additional exponential factor, which evolves in time like $\left(1 - \exp\left(-t/\tau_g\right)\right)$ for the build-up of the space charge field and $\exp\left(-t/\tau_g\right)$ for a decaying field. The time constant τ_g, which is crucial for the variation of the space charge field, is purely real for the case that no external field exists and no depletion of donors or acceptors occurs. In this case the factor $n_0^3 r_{\text{eff}} \tilde{E} \equiv n'_{\text{max}}$ from Eq. (3.17) can be interpreted as the saturation value of the refractive index grating with the time dependence

$$n'(t) = n'_{\text{max}} \cdot (1 - e^{-t/\tau_g}) \qquad \text{(build-up)} \tag{3.18}$$

$$n'(t) = n'_{\text{max}} \cdot e^{-t/\tau_g}. \qquad \text{(decay)} \tag{3.19}$$

3.2.3 Light Diffraction by Refractive Index Volume Gratings

The interaction of the constituting light field and the written refractive index grating can be highly complex. As soon as two beams start to establish a grating, either is diffracted at the grating, again influencing the further development of the grating. In this section, a short description of the coupled wave theory is given, which allows for a precise understanding of the dynamics involved in two-wave mixing in photorefractive crystals in general. Furthermore, an interference model is discussed that is based on the coupled wave equations and can provide a more convenient and intuitive description in particular for applications in holographic data storage or real-time interferometry.

Coupled wave equations

Equation (3.17) gives the stationary refractive index grating that is constituted by two light waves incident at an angle 2Θ. The influence of the grating on the writing beams can be described starting with the time-independent wave equation for the total light field $E = S(\vec{r}) + R(\vec{r})$

$$\nabla^2 E + \frac{\omega^2}{c^2} n^2 E = 0, \tag{3.20}$$

with the light (angular) frequency ω and velocity c. For the sake of simplicity in the following it will be assumed that both incident waves propagate in the x-z plane.

Assuming further that the slowly varying envelop approximation and the paraxial approximation are valid, the steady state coupled differential equations for two-wave mixing can be derived (Krishnamachari 2005; Yeh 1993):

$$\frac{d}{dz}\hat{S} = -\frac{1}{2I_0}\Gamma|\hat{R}|^2\hat{S} \tag{3.21}$$

$$\frac{d}{dz}\hat{R} = +\frac{1}{2I_0}\Gamma^*|\hat{S}|^2\hat{R}. \tag{3.22}$$

The complex value

$$\Gamma = i\frac{2\pi n'_{\max}}{\lambda\cos\theta}e^{-i\phi} = \gamma + i2\beta \tag{3.23}$$

is the coupling constant with the real part γ and the imaginary part 2β (Krishna-machari 2005).

The differential Eqs. (3.21) and (3.22) can be separated for the intensities and phases of the incident waves. With intensities defined consistently with the previous usage ($I_S = |S|^2 = |\hat{S}|^2$, $I_R = |R|^2 = |\hat{R}|^2$, and $I_0 = I_S + I_R$), solving these differential equations for the output intensities yields (Yeh 1993)

$$I_S(L) = I_S(0)\frac{1+m^{-1}}{1+m^{-1}e^{\gamma L}} \tag{3.24}$$

$$I_R(L) = I_R(0)\frac{1+m}{1+me^{-\gamma L}}, \tag{3.25}$$

where $m = I_S(0)/I_R(0)$ stands for the intensity ratio of the incident waves. The output phases for incident complex amplitudes $\hat{S} = |\hat{S}|e^{-i\Psi_S}$ and $\hat{R} = |\hat{R}|e^{-i\Psi_R}$ are given as (Yeh 1993):

$$\Psi_S(L) = \Psi_S(0) - \frac{\beta}{\gamma}\ln\left(\frac{1+m^{-1}}{1+m^{-1}e^{\gamma L}}\right) \tag{3.26}$$

$$\Psi_R(L) = \Psi_R(0) + \frac{\beta}{\gamma}\ln\left(\frac{1+m}{1+me^{-\gamma L}}\right). \tag{3.27}$$

Furthermore, the intensity diffraction efficiency from Eq. (3.9) can be refined and written in terms of intensity ratio and coupling constants (Kukhtarev et al. 1979; Krishnamachari et al. 2005):

$$\eta = \frac{2me^{-\gamma L/2}}{1+m}\left(\frac{\cosh(\gamma L/2) - \cos\beta L}{1+me^{-\gamma L}}\right). \tag{3.28}$$

Interference model

The diffraction and interference inherent in two-wave mixing can be exposed by an interference model (Krishnamachari 2005; Krishnamachari et al. 2005; Yarrison-Rice et al. 1995; Sedlatschek 1998; Sedlatschek et al. 1999). Therefore, the interference between the transmitted part of S and the diffracted part of R and vice versa is considered. For the incident intensities I_S and I_R and a diffraction efficiency η, the output intensities from Eqs. (3.24) and (3.25) can be rewritten as (Krishnamachari 2005):

$$I_S(L) = (1 - \eta)I_S(0) + \eta I_R(0) + 2\sqrt{\eta(1-\eta)I_S(0)I_R(0)} \cos(\phi + \chi(L) + \pi/2)$$
$$(3.29)$$

$$I_R(L) = (1 - \eta)I_R(0) + \eta I_S(0) + 2\sqrt{\eta(1-\eta)I_S(0)I_R(0)} \cos(\phi + \chi(L) - \pi/2).$$
$$(3.30)$$

The phase shift of $\pi/2$ in the cosine term occurs due to diffraction of one beam at the refractive index grating in either case. The phase term χ depends on the coupling constants γ, β and the intensity ratio m. It can be calculated analytically following (Krishnamachari 2005)

$$\chi(z) = \sin^{-1}\left(\frac{\sinh\alpha\cos\beta z - \sinh\delta}{\sqrt{\sinh^2\alpha + \sinh^2\delta + \sin^2\beta z - 2\sinh\alpha\sinh\delta\cos\beta z}}\right), \quad (3.31)$$

with $\alpha = \ln\sqrt{m}$ and $\delta = \alpha - \gamma z/2$.

In comparison with the coupled wave equations, the description of two-beam coupling with the interference model has the advantage that it directly points out the dependence on the grating parameters η and χ. However, it has to be borne in mind that the interference model does not include any time-dependence. Nevertheless, it can be used, with the appropriate amount of care, if the refractive index grating can be considered as quasi-static, i.e. it changes with time only slowly compared to the effects to be described (Vahey 1975).

Holographic real-time interferometry (Vest 1979; Frejlich et al. 1989) is one application where the interference model is well suited for a good understanding of the underlying physical principles. Here, information from an object is encoded in one of the beams, say S without loss of generality. This beam may be referred to as signal beam then as it carries information. A hologram is written with the signal beam and the other beam, R, as the reference beam. This hologram stores the amplitude and phase information of the object and serves as a reference. When the object changes in amplitude or phase, for example when it is deformed, the reconstructed part of the signal beam with the reference information is superimposed with the transmitted part of the signal beam with the new information. The output can be described according to Eq. (3.29). It contains information on the change of the objective encoded in the output intensity. With appropriate choices of m, χ,[4] and an additionally imprinted phase shift between S and R, the output can even be nullified before the expected change of the object, so that only the change is highlighted (Krishnamachari et al. 2005). If the selected photorefractive material is fast compared to the expected dynamics of the object and the parameter χ is such that the output is nullified in the stationary case, this particular dynamic holographic interferometer is well-known as an *optical novelty filter* (Krishnamachari 2005; Woerdemann et al. 2008; Cudney et al. 1988; Anderson et al. 1987).

---

[4] The grating parameter χ can be changed with the choice of the photorefractive material.

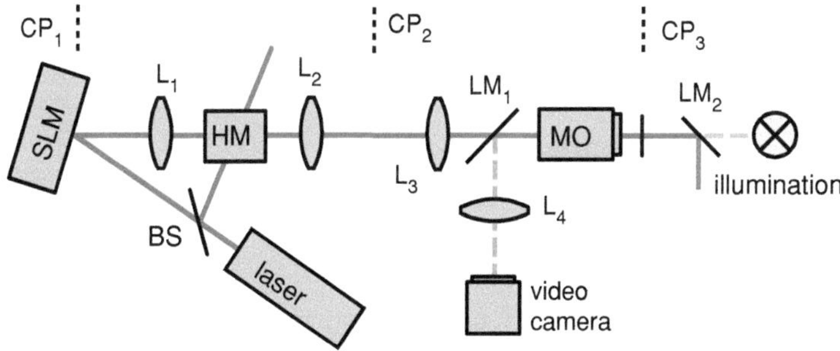

Fig. 3.3 Basic concept of HPC optical tweezers. CP_1, CP_2 and CP_3 are conjugate image planes. *SLM* phase only spatial light modulator; *HM* holographic storage material; *MO* microscope objective; L_1–L_4 imaging lenses; *LM* laser line mirrors; *BS* beam splitter

3.3 The Concept of Holographic Phase Contrast

In the present chapter, holographic phase contrast (HPC) is introduced as a novel method to generate dynamic intensity patterns from corresponding phase patterns in an image-plane approach. The achieved intensity patterns can be used in the field of optical micromanipulation, where the intensity distribution defines the optical potential landscape (cf. Eq. (2.5)).

Figure 3.3 shows the suggested concept of HPC for the application in optical micromanipulation. An optical microscope is combined with a phase-only SLM, which is imaged into the observation plane CP_3 of the microscope. The microscope consists of the illumination, the microscope objective (MO), the tube lens (L_4), and a video camera. Together with the MO, the tube lens creates a real image of CP_3 at the video camera. The SLM is illuminated by an expanded laser beam. After the SLM, the beam is downsized and the SLM is imaged by means of a Keplarian telescope, consisting of lenses L_1 and L_2, into an intermediate image plane CP_2. At this conjugate plane, the conversion from the phase distribution on the SLM to an intensity distribution has already been performed as will be explained in detail. By means of lens L_3 and the microscope objective, the image plane CP_2 is imaged into the trapping and observation plane CP_3 of the microscope. The laser beam path and the microscope image beam path are separated by two laser line mirrors that selectively reflect the laser wave length while transmitting all other wavelengths of the illumination. While the separation of the two beam paths could also be realised by other means as, for example, orthogonal polarisation states, the suggested configuration is common for standard optical tweezers (McGloin 2006). It is, however, important to note that, in contrast to holographic optical tweezers (cf. Chap. 7, Sect. 7.1.3), the SLM is not located in a Fourier plane with respect to the plane of trapping, but in a conjugate image plane.

The crucial part of the setup is the conversion from the phase distribution displayed on the SLM to a corresponding intensity distribution. This is done by holographic real-time interferometry in the holographic material HM. The material can be a

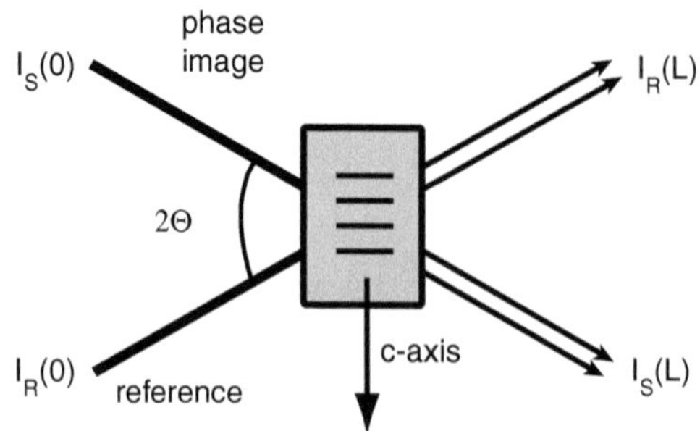

Fig. 3.4 Sketch of holographic interferometry in a photorefractive medium. Two beams with intensities $I_S(0)$ and $I_R(0)$ are incident on the medium with an angle 2Θ. $I_S(L)$ and $I_R(L)$ are the intensities after propagation of a distance L in the medium

photorefractive crystal, a photorefractive polymer, a photosensitive polymer or any material which allows to write and then read out a hologram and is self-developing (Magnusson et al. 1994). A photorefractive material has the advantage of a flexible writing, reading and erasure of holograms (Frejlich et al. 1989). Furthermore, photorefractive materials usually enable thick holograms that result in Bragg diffraction and thus prevent losses of light intensity into higher diffraction orders. The basic principle of holographic real-time interferometry can be described by the interference model (Eqs. (3.29) and (3.30)) and is sketched in Fig. 3.4. Two beams S, R with intensities $I_S(0)$ and $I_R(0)$ are overlaid within a suitable material. The two beams generate an interference pattern, which is stored as a refractive index hologram, for example by the photorefractive effect. The hologram now acts as a Bragg grating and diffracts parts of $I_S(0)$ and $I_R(0)$ in the direction of the other beam with a diffraction efficiency η. As a result, the complete wavefront of each beam is stored in the material and read out by the other beam. If the complex amplitudes of the incident beams are $\hat{S} = \sqrt{I_S(0)}e^{-i\Psi_S(0)}$ and $\hat{R} = \sqrt{I_R(0)}e^{-i\Psi_R(0)}$ with an intensity ratio $m = I_S(0)/I_R(0)$, the output intensity of S after the holographic medium, i.e. $I_S(L)$, is given by Eq. (3.29) as:

$$I_S(L) = (1-\eta)I_S(0) + \eta I_R(0) + 2\sqrt{\eta(1-\eta)I_S(0)I_R(0)}\cos(\Delta\Psi_0 + \Phi). \quad (3.32)$$

Here, $\Delta\Psi_0 = \Psi_R(0) - \Psi_S(0)$ is the phase difference between the incident beams. Hence, a phase transfer function (PTF) can be given, which states the output intensity of one beam with the relative phase shift $\Delta\Psi_0$ as a parameter. The phase term Φ defines a working point, i.e. an offset on the phase axis which can be chosen by an additionally introduced phase shift of one of the beams.

The optimum contrast of the PTF is received if the intensity ratio of the incident beams is chosen as (Krishnamachari et al. 2005):

$$m' = \frac{I_S'(0)}{I_R'(0)} = \frac{\eta}{1-\eta}. \quad (3.33)$$

In this case, the PTF then has a $\sin^2\left(\frac{1}{2}(\Delta\Psi_0 + \Phi)\right)$ dependence as shown in Fig. 3.6. It is important to note that there is no constraint on the absolute intensity of one beam at this point, but only the ratio is specified by Eq. (3.33). Therefore,

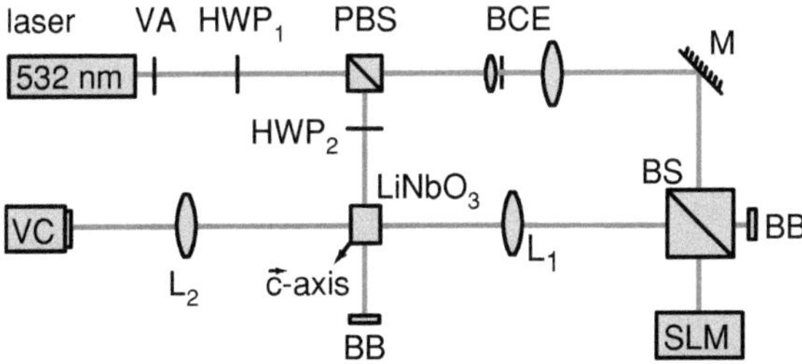

Fig. 3.5 Experimental setup of holographic phase contrast. L imaging lenses; $LiNbO_3$ photorefractive crystal; $(P)BS$ (polarising) beam splitter; HWP half wave plate; VA variable attenuator; BCE beam cleanup and expansion; BB beam blocker; M mirror; VC video camera

the output intensity can be chosen as required without further restrictions. The PTF contains all the information required for the envisaged phase to intensity conversion. If Eq. (3.33) is obeyed, any intensity value between 0 and $I_{max} = 4(1 - \eta)I_S$ can be achieved if the corresponding phase shift is applied. This argument holds true for any point in the two-dimensional input phase pattern, e.g. for each pixel of the SLM. By this means, any two-dimensional intensity distribution can be created, with the resolution mainly given by the SLM resolution.

3.4 Experimental Details and Discussion

In the following, the experimental setup for the proof of feasibility of HPC is described and results are discussed. The experimental setup is depicted in Fig. 3.5. A frequency-doubled, diode-pumped solid-state Nd:YAG laser, emitting at $\lambda = 532$ nm with an output power of $P_{max} = 100$ mW is used as the light source. The combination of the half wave plate (HWP_1) and the polarizing beam splitter (PBS) enables the flexible adjustment of the intensity ratio m. With the variable attenuator (VA), a neutral density filter, the total intensity can be set. The holographic material is chosen to be a photorefractive $45°$-cut $LiNbO_3$ crystal, since this material enables flexible writing and erasing of volume holograms (Volk and Wöhlecke 2008). Extraordinary polarisation, i.e. linearly p-polarised light in the depicted configuration, was used. The SLM is a commercially available Hamamatsu X8267-16 phase-only modulator, which operates in reflection geometry. This setup provides a versatile platform to investigate the basic properties of HPC.

The most important characteristics of the HPC system are gathered in the PTF. For the determination of the PTF, two steps are necessary. First, a reference hologram is stored. The time constant τ for the writing process depends on the total intensity used. For the discussed experiments, total laser powers in the order of $P = 10$ mW were used, with a spot size on the photorefractive material of about $d = 1 \, \text{mm}^2$. The reference hologram is written for about $t = 5$ min until the diffraction efficiency

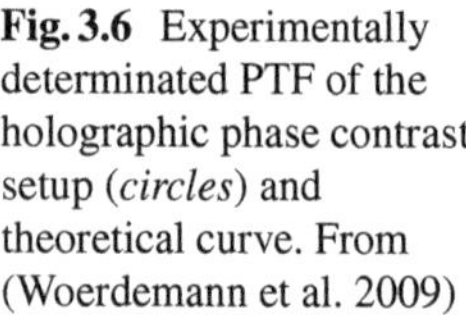

Fig. 3.6 Experimentally determined PTF of the holographic phase contrast setup (*circles*) and theoretical curve. From (Woerdemann et al. 2009)

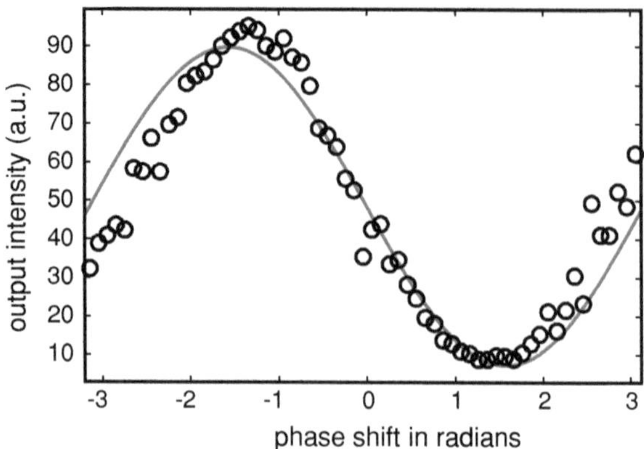

of the hologram approaches its saturation value. Then, the setup is prepared for the second step, the determination of the PTF. For this purpose, one of the input beams is shifted in phase with respect to the other, and by this means a phase interval of 2π is scanned. Typically, in similar experimental configurations, the reference beam is shifted, for example with a piezoelectric mirror (Krishnamachari and Denz 2004). In the present setup, the phase-only SLM is employed for this task. Therefore, the phase modulator is addressed with a homogeneous phase shift from 0 to 2π, in steps of 0.1π radians. Figure 3.6 shows a typical, measured phase transfer function for the discussed setup. The intensity values are measured as grey values on a calibrated (CCD) video camera, averaged over the whole sensor.

Having the PFT determined, a phase distribution which effects the desired intensity pattern, i.e. the trapping geometry, is easily designed. The phase of the envisaged (dark) background is chosen in such a way that that it corresponds to a minimum in the PTF. The (bright) traps are chosen so that the phase shift corresponds to another value, for example a maximum, in the PTF. In Fig. 3.7a, a typical configuration of five optical traps in a symmetric geometry is sketched. Figure 3.7b shows the accordingly designed phase pattern and Fig. 3.7c a corresponding experimental result. Clearly, the phase pattern is transferred to a corresponding intensity pattern. The background has a mean intensity of 66 grey values as measured with the calibrated video camera. The intensity spots which correspond to the desired optical traps have a mean of 190 grey values. This implies a ratio of roughly 1:3 and means that a not negligible part of the incident laser power cannot be utilised for optical trapping. It is important to understand that this is not a conceptional problem of HPC. The PTF in Fig. 3.6 already results in a ratio of better than 1:10, defining an approximate limit of the current experimental setup. The theoretical limit to the ratio is zero, since the dark background is the result of destructive interference which obviously can be total if the interfering intensities are chosen to be equal.

The most obvious use of HPC is the flexible generation of multiple point traps (Fig. 3.8a). It is interesting to mention that there is no principle limit—except for the SLM resolution—to the number of independent traps. This is due to the fact that

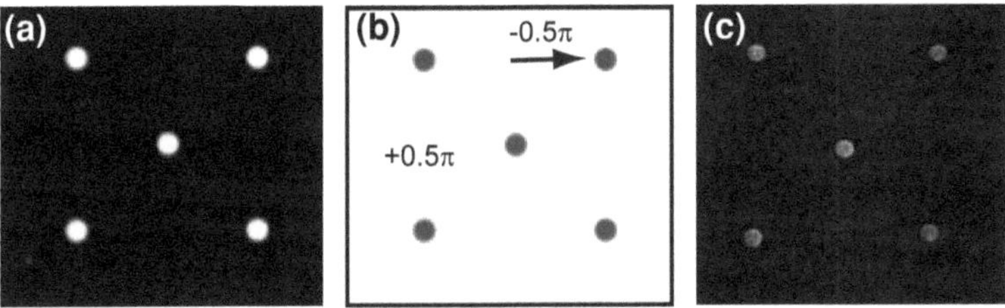

Fig. 3.7 **a** Desired trapping geometry. **b** Corresponding phase mask, where the *grey* values indicate the relative phase (*white* $+0.5\pi$ radians, *black* -0.5π radians). **c** Resulting intensity distribution after conversion by holographic phase contrast (experimental result)

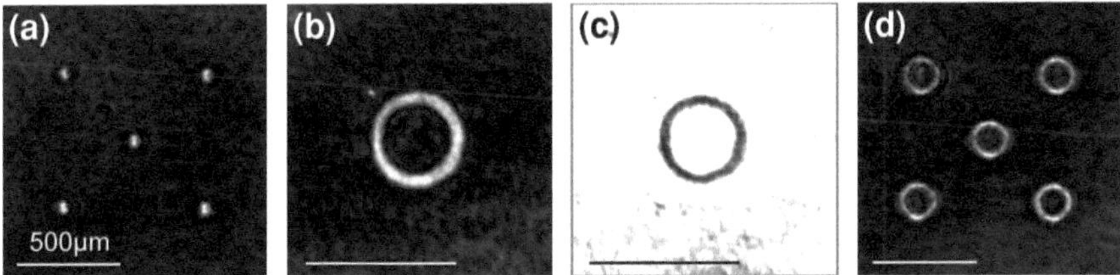

Fig. 3.8 Examples of trapping geometries. 5 single traps (**a**), a ring trap (**b**), an inverted ring trap (**c**), and a cluster of smaller ring traps (**d**)

energy is coupled into the traps from the reference beam. Other (common path) phase contrast (Zernike 1955; Glückstad 1996) methods would require all intensity to pass the SLM and intensity is redistributed from dark to bright areas. In consequence, the intensity per trap reduces with increasing number of traps (Daria et al. 2003).

Figure 3.8b shows another example, a circular trap. This configuration can be used, for example, to confine high index[5] objects to the ring or to enclose low index particles (Sasaki et al. 1992; MacDonald et al. 2001) or absorbing (Sasaki et al. 1992; Desyatnikov et al. 2009) particles inside the circle. Furthermore, the ring can be filled with high index particles to enclose an object inside that has an index of refraction very close to the surrounding medium and cannot be trapped directly. Figure 3.8c shows an inverted geometry with a dark ring on bright background. The dark ring should be a barrier for high index particles because the intensity gradient is negative (cf. Eq. (2.3)) and thus could be used to separate different particles from each other. It should also be possible to trap low-index or absorbing particles on the dark ring (Garces-Chavez et al. 2002). Of course, these are only basic examples and arbitrarily complex intensity distributions can be generated, with manifold possible applications in optical trapping. As a slightly more sophisticated example, an array of five smaller circles, is shown in Fig. 3.8d.

---

[5] High-index particles are particles with a refractive index higher than the surrounding medium while low-index particles are the reverse.

3.4.1 The Optimal Holographic Material

Photorefractive $LiNbO_3$ is suited for the proof-of-principle of the HPC concept due to its high flexibility. A hologram can be written easily and erased afterwards. For applications in optical micromanipulation, however, a material is desired in which a hologram can be written and afterwards read out without erasure. If the hologram is erased during operation, the quasi-static assumption of the interference model only permits operation life significantly shorter than the erasure time. Optical trapping usually requires light intensities that high that significant erasure takes place in $LiNbO_3$ after only a few minutes or even less.

Many different concepts are suitable to provide permanent holograms. For example, a wide range of fixing techniques (Buse et al. 1998; An et al. 1999) allow preserving a hologram written in photorefractive materials. Another option, which is attractive in view of commercial production, is the use of self-developing photosensitive polymers (Naydenova et al. 2004). These materials allow writing a hologram which either develops itself or by short homogeneous illumination and can be read out without any loss afterwards. It is very convenient that the requirements to the optimal material for HPC are mostly identical to the requirements of low-cost, read-once-write-many (WORM) holographic media, which currently are investigated intensively due to their importance for the consumer market. As a result, there is already a good choice of suitable materials available, which will probably enlarge even more.

With the optimal volume holographic material, HPC will be straightforward to use. The material is simply placed in the optical path without the need for very accurate alignment, as it is required for example for the phase plate in other phase contrast methods (Glückstad and Mogensen 2001). The signal beam then is overlaid inside the material with the reference beam and the reference hologram is written while the SLM is addressed with a homogeneous relative phase shift of 0. This has to be done only once, before the optical trapping system is used for the very first time. After that, the system can be used without any further modifications in the setup. It should be mentioned that thermal drift can cause a de-calibration of the system which cannot be compensated by the hologram if it is of a non-volatile type. There are two possible solutions to this issue. First, there are reversible fixation techniques that utilise a second light wave with a different (ultraviolet) wavelength (Buse et al. 1998). With the second beam present the hologram can be written, erased, or re-written; in the absence of ultraviolet light the hologram is non-volatile and can be read out without erasure. Second, the SLM enables full control of the wave front and, thus, is in principle able to compensate for any phase distortion introduced by thermal or other effects.

The optical quality of the created trapping geometry is essential for high-fidelity optical micromanipulation. A comprehensive review of the optical properties of holographic media and their influences on the image quality is out of the scope of this thesis and can be found in literature, e.g. (Coufal et al. 2000). In short, there are materials with excellent optical quality available which should enable almost aberration free trapping geometries of very high image quality.

3.5 Conclusion and Perspectives

SLM-based concepts for the generation of multiple-beam optical tweezers can be assorted in holographic and image-plane methods. Both concepts usually rely on phase-only SLMs in order to minimise absorption losses by the SLM and exploit the major part of the laser power. HOT generally require relatively time-consuming calculations to generate the phase-distribution that corresponds to a desired trapping geometry. In image-plane methods such as HPC (Woerdemann et al. 2009) or generalised phase contrast (Eriksen et al. 2002), the SLM generates a phase distribution which is transferred by a phase contrast technique into an intensity distribution. This intensity distribution corresponds to the final trapping geometry and is imaged into the trapping plane of the optical tweezers. HPC shares the principal advantages of other image-plane methods in comparison to HOT (Mogensen and Glückstad 2000). In particular, there are no time-consuming calculations required to generate a specific trapping geometry. Any desired geometry can be created in real-time, neglecting response times of the controller unit and the SLM. In this context, it is not a contradiction that writing the reference hologram in HPC may take a longer time—depending on the material and laser power—in the order of seconds to minutes. The reference hologram is written only once before the system is used for the first time. After that, the reference hologram is merely read out, which happens instantaneously and does not add any delay in the phase contrast process.

There is one significant difference between HPC and other image-plane or holographic methods. While most methods require all laser power to pass the SLM, in HPC the laser power which is used to trap objects has to pass the modulator only partially. This difference addresses one of the main limitations of all modulator based optical tweezers concepts. The modulator usually is the bottleneck if high trapping forces and a larger number of traps are required because its damage threshold is an unavoidable limit to the maximal laser power. With HPC, a part of the laser power is passed by the modulator. This advantage scales with the number of traps. In the case of only a few traps, HPC will perform similarly to other image-plane methods. However, with an increasing number of traps, the available power per trap in other approaches diminishes because laser power is redistributed from areas without traps to areas with traps. This becomes less efficient the more traps are desired (Daria et al. 2003). The available power per trap in HPC does not scale with the number of traps. The maximum power is constant, in the case of one as well as in the case of hundreds of traps, since laser power is coupled into the trap by the reference beam. The homogeneity of the intensity distribution between different traps of the same intentional force depends solely on the homogeneity of the SLM illumination. In particular, no ghost traps or traps with varying trapping force occur, as is often the case in holographic optical tweezers (Polin et al. 2005). Finally, no laser power is lost to the zeroth diffraction order and no measure has to be taken in order to moderate the zeroth order.

In summary, holographic phase contrast is a promising method to generate multiple or complex optical traps, dynamically and in real-time. HPC shares the basic advantages of other image-plane concepts and addresses the fundamental drawback of any optical trapping approach which involves spatial light modulators. HPC utilises two-wave mixing and by this means allows passing a significant part of the laser power by the SLM, thereby avoiding the bottleneck. The further development of HPC should concentrate on an extensive study of the various possible holographic materials with emphasis on optical quality, concepts of conditional (switchable) non-volatility, and tolerance to high operation powers in the order of tens to hundreds of milliwatts.

References

An X, Psaltis D, Burr G (1999) Thermal fixing of 10,000 holograms in $LiNbO_3$: Fe. Appl Opt 38:386–393

Anderson D, Lininger D, Feinberg J (1987) Optical tracking novelty filter. Opt Lett 12:123–125

Ashkin A, Boyd G, Dziedzic J, Smith R, Ballmann A, Levinstein J, Nassau K (1966) Optically-induced refractive index inhomogenities in $LiNbO_3$ and $LiTaO_3$. Appl Phys Lett 9:72

Berger G (2008) Volume holographic data storage utilizing phase modulations. PhD thesis, Westfälische Wilhelms-Universität Münster

Buse K, Adibi A, Psaltis D (1998) Non-volatile holographic storage in doubly doped lithium niobate crystals. Nature 393:665–668

Coufal H, Psaltis D, Sincerbox G (eds) (2000) Holographic data storage. Springer, Berlin

Cudney R, Pierce R, Feinberg J (1988) The transient detection microscope. Nature 332:424–426

Curtis J, Koss B, Grier D (2002) Dynamic holographic optical tweezers. Opt Commun 207:169–175

Daria V, Eriksen R, Glückstad J (2003) Dynamic optical manipulation of colloidal systems using a spatial light modulator. J Mod Opt 50:1601–1614

Desyatnikov A, Shvedov V, Rode A, Krolikowski W, Kivshar Y (2009) Photophoretic manipulation of absorbing aerosol particles with vortex beams: theory versus experiment. Opt Express 17:8201–8211

Dufresne E, Grier D (1998) Optical tweezer arrays and optical substrates created with diffractive optics. Rev Sci Instrum 69:1974–1977

Dufresne E, Spalding G, Dearing M, Sheets S, Grier D (2001) Computer-generated holographic optical tweezer arrays. Rev Sci Instrum 72:1810–1816

Eriksen RL, Mogensen PC, Glückstad J (2002) Multiple-beam optical tweezers generated by the generalized phase-contrast method. Opt Lett 27:267–269

Frejlich J, Kamshilin A, Kulikov V, Mokrushina E (1989) Adaptive holographic-interferometry using photorefractive crystals. Opt Commun 70:82–86

Garces-Chavez V, Volke-Sepulveda K, Chavez-Cerda S, Sibbett W, Dholakia K (2002) Transfer of orbital angular momentum to an optically trapped low-index particle. Phys Rev A 66:063402

Glückstad J (1996) Phase contrast image synthesis. Opt. Commun 130:225–230

Glückstad J, Mogensen P (2001) Optimal phase contrast in common-path interferometry. Appl Opt 40:268–282

Hariharan P (1996) Optical holography: principles, techniques and applications. Cambridge University Press, Cambridge

Hesseling C, Woerdemann M, Hermerschmidt A, Denz C (2011) Controlling ghost traps in holographic optical tweezers. Opt Lett 36:3657–3659

Jesacher A, Fürhapter S, Bernet S, Ritsch-Marte M (2004) Diffractive optical tweezers in the Fresnel regime. Opt Express 12:2243

Kogelnik H (1969) Coupled wave theory for thick hologram gratings. AT&T Tech J 48:2909

Krishnamachari V (2005) Photorefractive novelty filter microscope: the system and its applications. PhD thesis, Westfälische Wilhelms-Universität Münster

Krishnamachari V, Denz C (2004) A phase-triggering technique to extend the phase-measurement range of a photorefractive novelty filter microscope. Appl Phys B 79:497

Krishnamachari V, Grothe O, Deitmar H, Denz C (2005) Novelty filtering with a photorefractive lithium-niobate crystal. Appl. Phys Lett 87:071105

Kukhtarev N, Markov V, Odulov S, Soskin M, Vinetskii V (1979) Holographic storage in electro-optic crystals 1: steady state. Ferroelectrics 22:949–960

Kukhtarev N, Markov V, Odulov S, Soskin M, Vinetskii V (1979) Holographic storage in electro-optic crystals 2: beam-coupling—light amplification. Ferroelectrics 22:961–964

MacDonald M, Paterson L, Sibbett W, Dholakia K, Bryant P (2001) Trapping and manipulation of low-index particles in a two-dimensional interferometric optical trap. Opt Lett 26:863–865

Magnusson R, Wang X, Hafiz A, Black T, Tello L, Hajisheikh A, Konecni S, Wilson D (1994) Experiments with photorefractive crystals for holographic interferometry. Opt Eng 33:596–607

McGloin D (2006) Optical tweezers: 20 years on. Philos T Roy Soc A 364:3521–3537

Mogensen P, Glückstad J (2000) Dynamic array generation and pattern formation for optical tweezers. Opt Commun 175:75–81

Naydenova I, Jallapuram R, Howard R, Martin S, Toal V (2004) Investigation of the diffusion processes in a self-processing acrylamide-based photopolymer system. Appl Opt 43:2900–2905

Polin M, Ladavac K, Lee S, Roichman Y, Grier D (2005) Optimized holographic optical traps. Opt Express 13:5831–5845

Reicherter M, Haist T, Wagemann E, Tiziani H (1999) Optical particle trapping with computer-generated holograms written on a liquid-crystal display. Opt Lett 24:608–610

Rodrigo P, Daria V, Gluckstad J (2005) Four-dimensional optical manipulation of colloidal particles. Appl Phys Lett 86:074103

Sasaki K, Koshioka M, Misawa H, Kitamura N, Masuhara H (1992) Optical trapping of a metal particle and a water droplet by a scanning laser beam. Appl Phys Lett 60:807–809

Sedlatschek M (1998) Neuigkeitsfilter durch photorefraktive Strahlkopplung. PhD thesis, Technische Universität Darmstadt

Sedlatschek M, Trumpfheller J, Hartmann J, Müller M, Denz C, Tschudi T (1999) Differentiation and subtraction of amplitude and phase images using a photorefractive novelty filter. Appl Phys B 68:1047

Vahey D (1975) A nonlinear coupled-wave theory of holographic storage in ferroelectric materials. J Appl Phys 46:3510

Vest C (1979) Holographic interferometry. Wiley, New York

Volk T, Wöhlecke M (2008) Lithium Niobate—defects, photorefraction and ferroelectric switching. Springer, Berlin

Woerdemann M, Holtmann F, Denz C (2008) Full field particle velocimetry with a photorefractive optical novelty filter. Appl Phys Lett 93:021108

Woerdemann M, Holtmann F, Denz C (2009) Holographic phase contrast for dynamic multiple-beam optical tweezers. J Opt A: Pure Appl Opt 11:034010

Woerdemann M, Alpmann C, Denz C (2012) Three-dimensional particle control by holographic optical tweezers. In: Osten W, Reingand N (eds) Optical imaging and metrology. Wiley-VCH Verlag, Weinheim, to be published

Yarrison-Rice J, Rice P, Rowan D (1995) Beam splitter model of two-beam coupling in photorefractive materials. J Mod Opt 42:1971

Yeh P (1993) Introduction to photorefractive nonlinear optics. Wiley, New York

Zernike F (1955) How I discovered phase contrast. Science 121:345–349

Chapter 4
Counter-Propagating Traps by Optical Phase-Conjugation

"Classical" optical tweezers employ one single laser beam that is strongly focussed by one lens. In spite of a long list of advantages, which are discussed comprehensively in Chap. 2, there are a number of situations where the requirement for high numerical aperture objectives is a serious obstacle or where the inherent asymmetry of the configuration is an issue. One well known solution is counter-propagating optical traps, which are widely used where long working distances, axially symmetric trapping potentials, or standing light waves are desired. In this chapter, optical phase-conjugation is introduced as a particularly sophisticated means to automatically provide counter-propagating replicas of a wide range of incident light fields in an optical trapping configuration. The resulting counter-propagating traps are self-adjusting and adapt dynamically to changes of the input light field. It is shown that not only single or stationary counter-propagating traps can be implemented by phase-conjugation, but also spatio-temporally structured light fields can be used.[1]

4.1 Counter-Propagating Optical Traps

In optical tweezers one laser beam is tightly focused (Ashkin et al. 1986)—usually through a microscope objective that is used for observation anyway (Martin-Badosa et al. 2007)—so that it can hold and trap microscopic particles without the aid of any other, counteracting forces (Ashkin 2000). The simplicity and elegance of this approach has led to a vast number of applications of optical tweezers (Svoboda and Block 1994; Neuman and Block 2004; Dholakia and Reece 2006), but they also suffer from fundamental limitations.

The most obvious limitation is the asymmetry of the configuration. As a direct consequence, the optical potential well is strongly asymmetric in axial direction with the weakest part being in beam propagation direction (cf. Fig. 2.3). Since the

---

[1] The experiments discussed in this chapter were performed in collaboration with Mr Konrad Berghoff within the framework of his diploma thesis (Berghoff 2010) and have resulted in a joint publication (Woerdemann et al. 2010).

M. Woerdemann, *Structured Light Fields*, Springer Theses,
DOI: 10.1007/978-3-642-29323-8_4, © Springer-Verlag Berlin Heidelberg 2012

scattering force in the direction of the pointing vector and, hence, the beam axis can only be compensated by a sufficiently high axial gradient force, stable optical tweezers require very strong axial intensity gradients, which can only be achieved with high numerical aperture lenses. This requirement for the objective lens limits the available working distance[2] between objective and specimen to a few hundred micrometers and makes the use of immersion fluid unavoidable (Sinclair et al. 2004). Furthermore, the requirement of a strongly focused laser beam inevitably results in extreme local intensities and additionally imposes strict constraints on aberrations of the optical system (Tauro et al. 2010).

An interesting alternative to optical tweezers is counter-propagating (CP) optical traps, where the scattering force in the direction of beam propagation is counterbalanced by an opposed second beam. The concept of CP optical traps is much older then the concept of single beam optical tweezers. Already the pioneering works in optical trapping (Ashkin 1970) discussed and demonstrated a CP optical trap configuration and the concept has always been in the focus of research for applications where high working distance, low light pollution, or axially symmetric trapping potentials are more important than a simple implementation. The utilisation of CP beams, however, has much more fundamental implications (Petrovic et al. 2011). The available solid angle of incident k-vectors at the focal plane is extended from 2π—the ideal case if one beam and one microscope objective are used—to up to 4π. This enables, for example, the creation of standing light waves that are structured in axial direction and enable exciting applications like optical sorting or a particularly strong axial confinement (Jonas and Zemanek 2008). All but the simplest implementations of CP traps where a mirror is placed directly in the specimen plane (Zemanek et al. 1999, Zwick et al. 2009) have in common that they are relatively complex, compared to optical tweezers, and accurate alignment can be complicated (Dam et al. 2007a, 2007b). If typical state-of-the-art features like multiple traps and individual, flexible positioning in all three dimensions are required, the complexity even increases (Rodrigo et al. 2005).

Figure 4.1 provides an overview of different configurations of CP optical traps. The configuration with overlapping foci in Fig. 4.1a enables the best exploitation of the available light intensity. The complete overlap results in a compensation of the axial scattering forces at any location along the beams and thus only the gradient forces are to be considered. For symmetry reasons, the stable trapping position is at the position of the beam waists, if both beams have the same intensity. If the intensity ratio of both beams is varied, the equilibrium position shifts only slightly or becomes unstable; for significant axial displacement, the focal planes have to be repositioned (Tauro et al. 2010). Hence, in many applications a configuration according to Fig. 4.1b is preferred (Rodrigo et al. 2006), where the foci are separated by a positive distance d. In this configuration, an axial equilibrium position does exist, even if both beams feature significantly different intensities (Rodrigo et al. 2006). Variation of

---

[2] Remember that numerical aperture NA and focal length are connected as $\mathrm{NA} = n\sin(\Theta/2) = n\sin\arctan(a/f) \approx na/f$ for a lens with the aperture angle Θ and the aperture diameter $2a$ (Born and Wolf 1986).

the intensity ratio is thus a convenient means of shifting the axial trapping position. A different situation arises if the foci are separated by a negative distance $-d$ (Fig. 4.1c). This configuration is inherently unstable (Ashkin and Dziedzic 1985) and stable trapping is only possible with active feedback (Bowman et al. 2011) or rapid alternation with a stable configuration (Ashkin and Dziedzic 1985). The CP beams do not necessarily have to emerge from a free-space optical system with a terminating (microscope objective) lens. An interesting alternative can be implemented with opposing optical fibres (Fig. 4.1d), where configurations resembling Fig. 4.1b or c can be achieved, depending on the curvature of the polished fibre ends (Constable et al. 1993, Guck et al. 2002). One particularly ingenious realisation of CP optical traps uses a mirror in the specimen plane in order to generate the back-propagating beam that opposes an incident beam. In its simplest implementation as depicted in Fig. 4.1e, the mirror is placed close to the beam waist of the incident beam (Zemanek et al. 1999) and the stable trapping position would be at the mirror plane if incoherent waves are assumed as in all previous examples. Owing to the specific configuration, however, the CP beams can be considered mutually coherent up to a distance $l_c/2$ from the mirror, where l_c indicates the coherence length of the incident beam. The coherence results in standing light waves with stationary intensity maxima, separated by half a wavelength in axial direction, which can be used to trap dielectric particles small enough compared to the wavelength (Zemanek et al. 2002, 2003). Holographic beam shaping allows generating multiple beams with tunable divergence. By this means, two beams can be generated—one having its beam waist in front of the mirror and the other one having its beam waist only after reflection (Fig. 4.1f). This approach is versatile; for example all configurations from Fig. 4.1a–c can be emulated (Zwick et al. 2009, Thalhammer et al. 2011). However, it is not always desirable or even possible to have a highly reflecting optical element in the specimen plane. Furthermore, detailed knowledge of the geometry of the sample chamber is required in order to place each individual trap correctly, especially in complex, dynamic applications scenarios.

In this chapter, a method is presented and investigated that utilises optical phase-conjugation (PC) to realise CP optical traps. A photorefractive phase-conjugate mirror is used to create a back-propagating beam that automatically matches an arbitrary incident beam. This implementation is intrinsically self-aligning. It is demonstrated that not only single optical traps can be generated by this means. The concept can be extended to multiple traps and even dynamically reconfigured traps are possible.

4.2 Optical Phase-Conjugation

At this point we will go one step back and take a brief look at the basic principles of optical PC. Assuming an incident wave $\tilde{\vec{E}}_s(\vec{r}, t) = \vec{E}_s(\vec{r}) \exp(-i\omega t) + \text{cc}$,[3] we define its phase-conjugate replica as $\tilde{\vec{E}}_c(\vec{r}, t) = r\vec{E}_s^{\,*}(\vec{r}) \exp(-i\omega t) + \text{cc}$ with the

---

[3] The term "cc" indicates the complex conjugate, necessary to describe a real wave in the mathematical and physical sense.

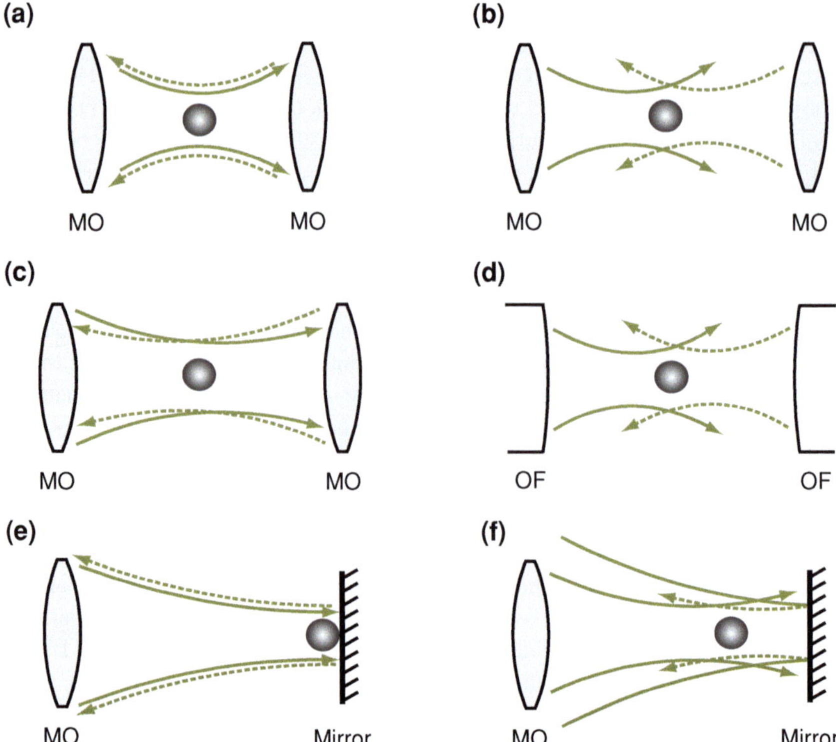

Fig. 4.1 Overview of different configurations of CP optical traps. Conventional implementations with opposing microscope objective lenses (**a**)–(**c**), optical fibres (**d**), and a single lens and a mirror in the sample plane (**e**), (**f**). *MO* microscope objective lens, *OF* optical fibre

amplitude reflection coefficient r. Furthermore, with $\vec{E}_s(\vec{r}) = \hat{\vec{\epsilon}} A_s(\vec{r}) \exp(i\vec{k}_s\vec{r})$ we introduce the complex polarisation unit vector $\hat{\vec{\epsilon}}$ that describes the polarisation state and require $\vec{E}_s^{\,*}(\vec{r}) = \hat{\vec{\epsilon}}^* A_s^*(\vec{r}) \exp(-i\vec{k}_s\vec{r})$. With these conventions, the important properties of optical PC are easily identified (Boyd 1992):

1. $A_s(\vec{r}) \rightarrow A_s^*(\vec{r})$: The spatial phase distribution is transferred into its complex conjugate—hence the name *phase-conjugation*—and thus the wave front is reversed.
2. $\vec{k}_s \rightarrow -\vec{k}_s$: The wave is exactly reflected back; in a ray optics description this means each ray is precisely reflected back onto itself.
3. $\hat{\vec{\epsilon}} \rightarrow \hat{\vec{\epsilon}}^*$: The polarisation unit vector is complex conjugated. For example, right-hand circular light remains right-hand circular light.

There are a number of experimental implementations of optical PC that usually do not or only partly possess all three properties (He 2002). In the following, an implementation by means of four-wave mixing is discussed and actual experimental designs are considered.

4.2.1 Degenerate Four-Wave Mixing

One of the fundamentals in linear optics is the assumption that the (time dependent) electric field and the resulting (electronic) polarisation in any material are linearly related as $\tilde{P}(t) = \chi^{(1)} \tilde{E}(t)$. The proportionality constant $\chi^{(1)}$ is known as susceptibility or, to distinguish it from the following, linear susceptibility. In general, to allow describing nonlinear effects, we need to account for higher order terms of the polarisation

$$\tilde{P}(t) = \chi^{(1)} \tilde{E}(t) + \chi^{(2)} \tilde{E}^2(t) + \chi^{(3)} \tilde{E}^3(t) + \cdots \tag{4.1}$$

with $\chi^{(2)}$ and $\chi^{(3)}$ being the second and third order susceptibilities. For many materials, in particular centrosymmetric crystals, $\chi^{(2)}$ can be neglected and the third order susceptibility is dominant. For these materials the refractive index can be written as $n = n_0 + n_2 I$, i. e., the linear refractive index n_0 is complemented with a nonlinear, intensity-dependent part. The latter is directly proportional to the third order susceptibility $\chi^{(3)}$.

One nonlinear optical process that can produce optical PC is degenerate four-wave mixing (Hellwarth 1977). Four waves $E_i(\vec{r}, t)$ with $i = 1, 2, 3, 4$ interact in a suitable nonlinear material (cf. Fig. 4.2). E_1 and E_2 are pump waves that are required to be a phase-conjugate pair. Usually, this is experimentally realised with two counter-propagating plane waves, which by definition are phase-conjugate with respect to each other. The wave E_3 is the signal wave that is to be phase-conjugated and a phase-conjugate replica E_4 is produced. It can be shown (Boyd 1992) that the polarisation of the material can be described by:

$$P \propto \chi^{(3)} E_1 E_2 E_3^* = \chi^{(3)} A_1 A_2 A_3^* e^{i(\vec{k}_1 + \vec{k}_2 - \vec{k}_3)\vec{r}}. \tag{4.2}$$

Combining this result with the requirement of E_1 and E_2 being a phase-conjugate pair and hence

$$\vec{k}_1 = -\vec{k}_2 \tag{4.3}$$

$$A_1 = A_2^*, \tag{4.4}$$

we get

$$P \propto \chi^{(3)} |A_1|^2 A_3^* e^{-i\vec{k}_3 \vec{r}}. \tag{4.5}$$

This polarisation has a spatial dependence so that it gives rise to the new wave E_4 with the amplitude $A_4 \propto |A_1|^2 A_3^*$ and the wave vector $\vec{k}_4 = -\vec{k}_3$. This wave is the phase-conjugate replica of E_3.

The process of four-wave mixing can also be understood in terms of volume holography (cf. Sect. 3.2). Consider one of the pump beams, for example E_1. This beam interferes with the signal beam E_3 and produces a stationary interference pattern. By means of the underlying nonlinear process, this intensity distribution is transferred to a corresponding modulation of the refractive index. The other pump beam, E_2, is diffracted by the refractive index grating and thus reads out the "hologram". Since E_2 is not the original writing beam but a wave phase-conjugate with respect to the writing beam, it will read out a phase-conjugate wave of E_3, i. e. E_4.

4.2.2 Photorefractive Implementation

The photorefractive effect (cf. Sect. 3.2.2) has a different microscopic origin than the described nonlinear effects induced by (electronic) polarisation of the material. However, as it might be obvious from the volume holographic description of four-wave mixing above, the photorefractive effect can be used for the generation of optical PC as it provides intensity dependent refractive index modulations (Feinberg and Hellwarth 1980). The high nonlinearity of the photorefractive effect enables optical PC even at very low intensities. Another important difference of refractive index changes induced by the photorefractive effect compared to the above described nonlinear processes is their time-dependence. While electronic polarisation can be induced at time constants in the order of femtoseconds, the time constant of the photorefractive effect is intensity-dependent and usually ranges from tenths of a second to minutes (Boyd 1992).

Coupled wave equations

Similar to the coupled wave equations (Eqs. (3.21) and (3.22)) for the two-wave mixing process, a set of coupled differential equations can be derived for the four-wave mixing process in photorefractive materials. With the nomenclature of the complex amplitudes introduced in the preceding sections, one can write for the configuration depicted in Fig. 4.2 but using a suitable photorefractive material (Yeh 1993):

$$\frac{d}{dz}A_1 = \frac{1}{2I_0}\Gamma^* \left(A_3^* A_1 + A_2^* A_4\right) A_3 \tag{4.6}$$

$$\frac{d}{dz}A_2 = \frac{1}{2I_0}\Gamma \left(A_3 A_1^* + A_2 A_4^*\right) A_4 \tag{4.7}$$

$$\frac{d}{dz}A_3 = -\frac{1}{2I_0}\Gamma \left(A_3 A_1^* + A_2 A_4^*\right) A_1 \tag{4.8}$$

$$\frac{d}{dz}A_4 = \frac{1}{2I_0}\Gamma^* \left(A_3^* A_1 + A_2^* A_4\right) A_2, \tag{4.9}$$

with the complex constant Γ defined by Eq. (3.23) and the total intensity $I_0 = \sum_{i=1}^{4} |A_i|^2$. Assuming constant, undepleted pump waves E_1, E_2, the coupled equations can be solved for A_3 and A_4 (Yeh 1993) and the phase-conjugate

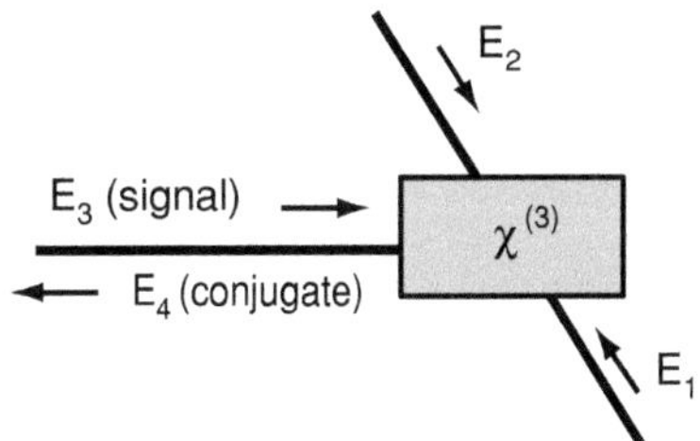

Fig. 4.2 Sketch of degenerate four-wave mixing in a nonlinear $\chi^{(3)}$ material. The incident signal wave E_3 is phase-conjugated (E_4) by means of two additional beams E_1, E_2, which are phase-conjugates of each other

reflection coefficient $\rho = A_4(0)/A_3^*(0)$ is obtained. With the pump intensity ratio $q = A_2/A_1$ and an interaction length L, the phase-conjugate reflectivity R is given by (Yeh 1993):

$$R = |\rho|^2 = \left| \frac{\sinh(\tfrac{1}{4}\Gamma L)}{\cosh(\tfrac{1}{4}\Gamma L - \ln\sqrt{q})} \right|^2. \tag{4.10}$$

The reflectivity can be significantly higher than one if the pump intensity ratio q is sufficiently high.

Self-pumped realisation

During the last decades, a vast number of photorefractive implementations of optical PC have been proposed and demonstrated (Croningolomb 1991). All these different configurations can be understood in term of four-wave mixing as depicted in Fig. 4.2 and they are optimised either for efficiency, simplicity, fidelity or a combination of those properties. One particularly elegant experimental realisation of such a photorefractive phase conjugating mirror (PCM) is the self-pumped variation depicted in Fig. 4.3.

For self-pumped photorefractive PC, a photorefractive material is utilised that exhibits two-beam intensity coupling as discussed in Sect. 3.2.3. Although only one beam (E_3) is incident on the photorefractive material, this beam scatters randomly at small imperfections that are always present (Zozulya 1993). Scattering happens in all directions, but only light scattered into the direction of two-beam coupling is amplified. After a short time that depends on the response time of the photorefractive material, incident intensity, and geometric configuration, this randomly induced process has exhibited a light fan into direction of the material's c-axis. With appropriately chosen geometry, this light fan can be directed into one corner of the material where it can be retro-reflected. Any ray of the light fan together with another reflected ray can be a pair of pump waves for the four-wave mixing process, for example E_1 and E_2, or E_1' and E_2' in Fig. 4.3. By this means, a new wave, E_4, is generated which is the phase-conjugate replica of the incident wave E_3 (Feinberg 1982). The self-pumped configuration is robust with respect to external influences as all interferometric parts are encased inside the material. Furthermore, it enables optical PC with high fidelity (Xie et al. 1997, Woerdemann et al. 2009). By implication, however,

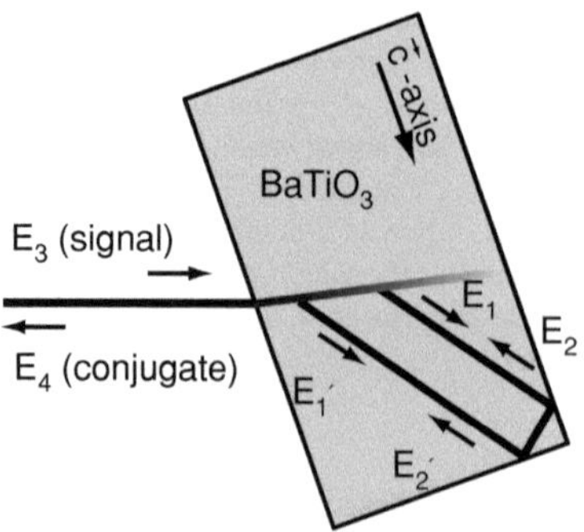

Fig. 4.3 Basic principle of self-pumped phase-conjugation in a photorefractive BaTiO$_3$ crystal.

reflectivity of a self-pumped configuration is limited to 100 %, with realistic values of 60–70%. An additional pump beam E_5 with significantly higher intensity than the signal beam (undepleted pump approximation) can be used to amplify the phase-conjugate wave further. Depending on the configuration, different physical principles of amplification are possible (Chiou 1999). If the additional pump beam also fulfills the geometrical conditions, i. e. point and angle of incidence, for self-pumped PC, it can share its internal pumping beams with the (weaker) actual signal beam (Feinberg 1983). In other configurations, the additional pump beam can transfer intensity by means of two-wave mixing into the signal beam or the conjugate beam. In either case the reflectivity as defined by the ratio of conjugate and signal beam intensity is increased.

Besides increased reflectivity, however, the external pump beam has additional merits. Consider, for example, a solely self-pumped configuration with a time-varying input signal. Since in this configuration all (internal) pump beams are derived from the signal beam, they need to be re-established at any relevant change of the input signal. The additional external pump beam not only decreases the response time due to the higher total intensity but can also provide stable internal pump beams even when the input signal changes significantly (Chiou 1999).

4.3 Phase-Conjugation for Counter-Propagating Traps

Perfect optical PC exactly reflects a light field into itself, thereby reversing propagation direction and phase front (Fisher 1983). This property led to the idea of using a PCM to create the back-propagating beam in a counter-propagating trap configuration (cf. Fig. 4.4b) (Wang et al. 1997). One compelling advantage over the conventional implementation with two separately prepared beams (Fig. 4.4a) is the inherent ability of the PCM to adapt dynamically to any change in the input light field. This means that the initial fine adjustment as well as any further readjustment, e. g. necessitated by unavoidable thermal drift of components, is done "automatically" by the system itself.

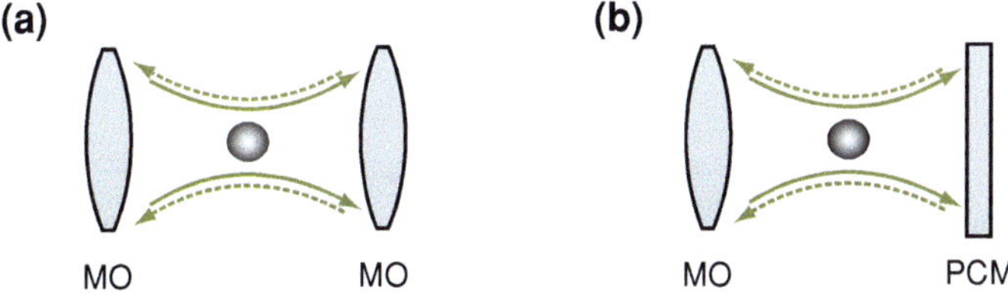

Fig. 4.4 Comparison between conventional CP optical trap configuration (**a**) and CP traps using optical phase-conjugation (**b**). *PCM*, phase-conjugating mirror.

There are some fundamental differences of phase-conjugate CP traps compared with conventional CP traps. In the conventional implementation, the relative position of the beam waists can be chosen freely, while in the (ideal) phase-conjugate implementation, the beam waists overlap perfectly by definition. Furthermore, in the phase-conjugate implementation both CP beams usually are mutually coherent in contrast to the conventional case, where the beams can be mutually coherent or not. However, in principle it is possible to tune the degree of mutual coherence in the phase-conjugate implementation by changing the propagation distance of the light between the sample plane and the PCM to values smaller or larger than the coherence length l_c of the utilised laser source. In many cases, however, coherence is desired, as it is the prerequisite for standing light wave traps (Zemanek et al. 1998).

The properties of a phase-conjugate CP trap are strongly related to the properties of the actually used implementation of the optical PC. In reality, for example, a PCM will not react instantaneously to a change in the incident light field, but will need a finite time τ to adapt the change. It is obvious that the two extreme cases of an almost instantaneous and a relatively slow implementation of the PCM lead to two completely different situations as soon as dynamics like the Brownian motion of the trapped particle or a change of the trapping configuration are considered.

4.3.1 Experimental Realisation

As seen earlier, optical PC can be realised through various nonlinear optical processes, such as four-wave mixing, three-wave mixing, backward stimulated scattering, and others (He 2002). For the experiments presented in the following, a self-pumped photorefractive implementation with an additional pump beam is utilised that relies on four-wave mixing inside a $BaTiO_3$ crystal as discussed in Sect. 4.2.2 (Feinberg and Hellwarth 1980, Woerdemann et al. 2009). This implementation has the advantage of being relatively easy to set up and providing high quality PC even with low light powers (in the order of milliwatts) (Woerdemann et al. 2009). Photorefractive PCMs feature comparatively large time constants τ (Croningolomb 1991) in the order of seconds, which makes it possible to analyse the dynamics of the CP traps in detail.

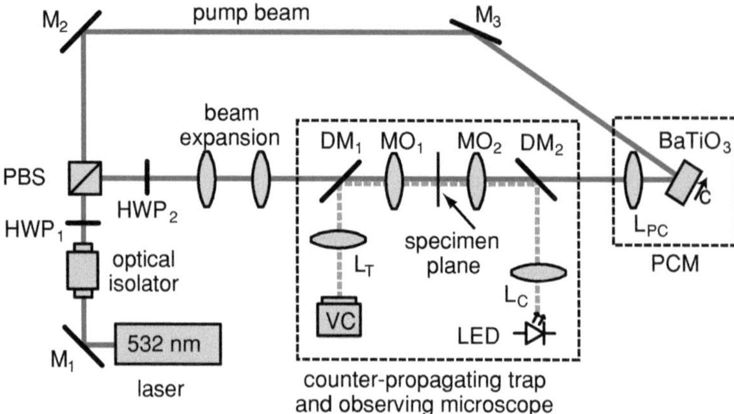

Fig. 4.5 Experimental setup for a single counter-propagating trap. *HWP* $\lambda/2$-plate; *DM* dichroic mirror, *MO* microscope objective, *VC* video camera, *LED* light-emitting diode, *L* lens, *M* mirror

The experimental setup for a single CP optical trap with optical PC is depicted in Fig. 4.5. It is based on the basic concept of Wang et al. (Wang et al. 1997), introducing a couple of modifications that mainly aim at a setup that is as simple as possible in order to facilitate a broad range of applications. The laser source is a frequency doubled Nd:YAG solid-state laser, emitting at a wavelength of $\lambda = 532\,\text{nm}$ with maximal output power of $P_{max} = 300\,\text{mW}$. After passing an optical isolator, the beam is variably split into the trap beam and a pump beam by means of a half-wave plate (HWP) and a polarising beams splitter (PBS). Polarisation of the trap beam is set to p-polarisation by another HWP and the trap beam is relayed and resized by a telescope and focused by microscope objective MO_1 with 40 x magnification and a numerical aperture $NA = 0.65$. After the specimen, the beam is collected by a second microscope objective (MO_2) with identical properties. The collected light is loosely focused through lens L_{PCM} into a nominally undoped $BaTiO_3$ photorefractive crystal which acts as the PCM. A pump beam, which is relayed by two mirrors (M), supplies the PCM with additional energy, thus enabling reflectivity of more than unity. With the implemented setup, maximal reflectivity of approximately $R_{max} = 280\,\%$ can be achieved.

The total transmittance of all components between specimen and PCM was measured to be $T = 85\,\%$. In order to achieve equal power of the input beam and the back-propagating beam at the sample plane, the reflectivity thus should be set to approximately $R = 152\,\%$, assuming the specimen has a transmission of $T_{spec} = 91\%$. The time constant of the PCM depends on the type of crystal, the total intensity incident on the crystal, the ratio of signal and pump beam and the exact geometry, i. e. the overlap of the beams, the incidence angles and the position of the crystal. Typical time constants of the implemented setup are $\tau = (1..30)\,\text{s}$. For the single CP trap experiments, a time constant of $\tau_0 \approx 10\,\text{s}$ was chosen.

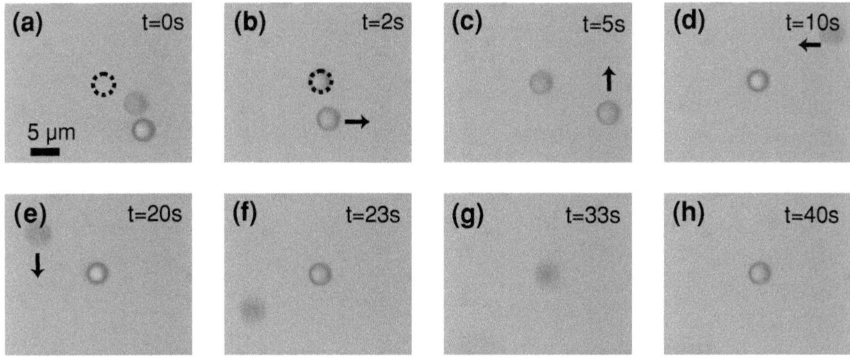

Fig. 4.6 Three dimensional trapping of a 4 µm polystyrene bead: the bead is trapped at the position of the *dashed circle* (**a**), (**b**) and the sample plane is translated transversally (**c**)–(**f**) and axially (**g**), (**h**), respectively. As the axial potential is relatively weak, the bead needs a few seconds to return to the trapping position in focus after axial displacement

An optical microscope is integrated by means of two dichroic mirrors (DM_1, DM_2) that reflect the laser wavelength and have a high transmission for the wavelength of the illumination. The microscope part consists of MO_1, acting as the observing microscope objective, the illumination, the tube lens L_T and a video camera. The illumination is provided by a red ($\lambda \approx 625$ nm) LED, a collimation lens L_C and MO_2, acting as the condenser.

The first evidence that the input beam is actually phase-conjugated rather than simply reflected is given by the observation that the beam exactly traces back its own path. It can be seen on the camera at the expected, correct position and even goes back into the laser, resulting in an unstable operation of the laser, if the optical isolator is omitted.

With this configuration, stable three-dimensional trapping of dielectric particles has been achieved. Typical values of laser power $P = 4$ mW (comprising both CP beams) in the trapping plane result in a transversal trap stiffness of $k = 2$pN/µm for $d = 4$ µm polystyrene beads. A trapped bead remains confined in the trap when the sample holder is translated in transverse or axial direction, respectively, as shown in Fig. 4.6. From the simple observation of the relaxation times of a particle displaced from its equilibrium position, it can be concluded that the axial stiffness is significantly lower than the transverse stiffness. This is in agreement with the lower axial gradient forces, resulting from the low numerical aperture of the used microscope objectives (Bowman et al. 2011). In contrast to single beam optical tweezers, however, three-dimensional trapping is still possible in spite of the low NA (and hence high working distance) due to the compensated scattering forces.

4.4 Multiple Dynamic Counter-Propagating Traps

A single optical trap implemented using optical PC is already interesting from the fundamental physics point of view as well as for applications in all fields that require counter-propagating optical light fields (Wang et al. 1997). For state-of-the-art applications of optical trapping, however, it is important to have the option to use structured light fields like, for example, multiple traps and control them dynamically. In the following, the basic, elegant idea of CP traps using optical PC is developed further towards these application-driven needs.

4.4.1 Multiple Counter-Propagating Traps

An extension of the concept of a phase-conjugate CP trap to multiple-beam traps is required for many advanced applications. Two traps already extend the possible applications significantly (Hörner et al. 2010, Woerdemann et al. 2010). In Fig. 4.7, the extended experimental setup for a dual CP trap is depicted. An interferometric part consisting of a beam splitter (BS) and two mirrors originates two beams which can be steered independently by the mirrors. The two beams in general have a small mutual angle, resulting in a corresponding interference pattern at the back aperture of the microscope objective MO_1. The interference pattern has a sinusoidal modulation (cf. insets in Fig. 4.7 for images of the light intensities at the respective planes). MO_1 performs an optical Fourier transformation of the incident light field and thus creates the desired two traps in the sample plane. The second microscope objective MO_2 performs an analogous reverse Fourier transformation and yields an interference pattern at the objective's back aperture, which is similar to the pattern at the entrance of MO_1. This pattern is phase-conjugated and the phase-conjugate light field traces back the original. By this means, two CP traps are generated in the sample plane. Figure 4.8 demonstrates the trapping of two 4 μm polystyrene beads simultaneously. This extension to two individually steerable traps already allows for many advanced operations.

The concept of multiple traps originating in the discrete splitting of one laser beam into multiple, independently steerable beams can, in principle, be extended to any desired number of traps by adding a corresponding number of beam splitters and mirrors. In practice, however, this approach is not feasible for more than a few traps and it is relatively inflexible. On the other hand, it is easy to implement and thus the method of choice, if two or a few CP optical traps are required.

4.4.2 Dynamic Counter-Propagating Traps

For a most versatile optical trapping system, the advantageous features of phase-conjugate CP traps should be combined with the formidable flexibility of light fields

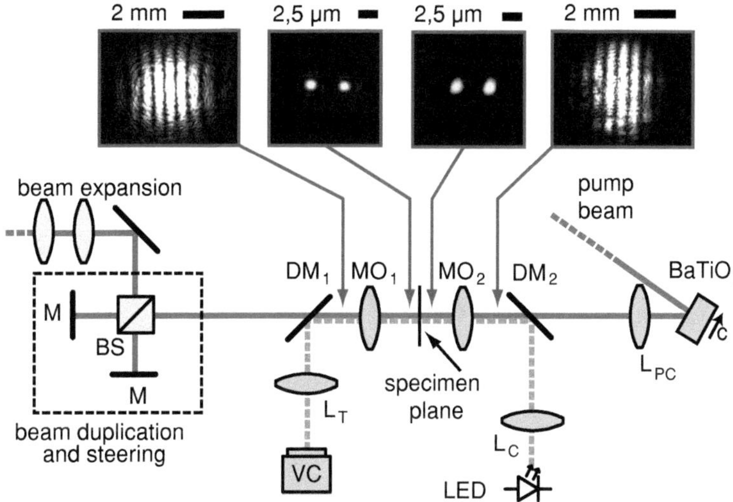

Fig. 4.7 Experimental setup for a dual counter-propagating trap. The origin of trap and pump beams is omitted. *Insets* show the measured intensity distribution at the indicated planes that arise from the incident wave

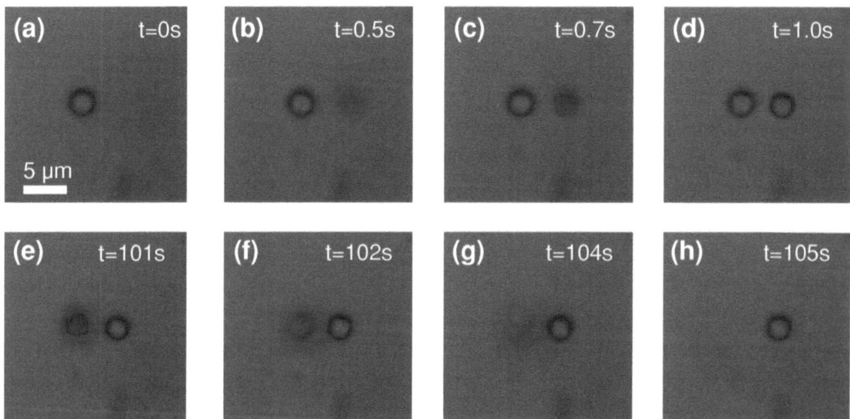

Fig. 4.8 Trapping of two $4\,\mu$m beads simultaneously. At $t = 0$ s only one trap is occupied (**a**). A second bead enters the other trap (**b**), (**c**) and both are trapped in a stable way (**d**) until the first bead is pushed out of the trap by another bead (**e**)–(**h**)

that are structured with SLMs. The extension of the setup towards SLM-shaped input light fields is depicted in Fig. 4.9. The SLM is illuminated with an expanded beam and then imaged onto the back aperture of MO_1 by lenses L_1 and L_2, in such a way that it exactly fits the back aperture area. By means of the optical Fourier transformation performed by MO_1, the desired trapping configuration is created, according to the calculated phase-pattern displayed on the SLM. After being recollected by MO_2, the

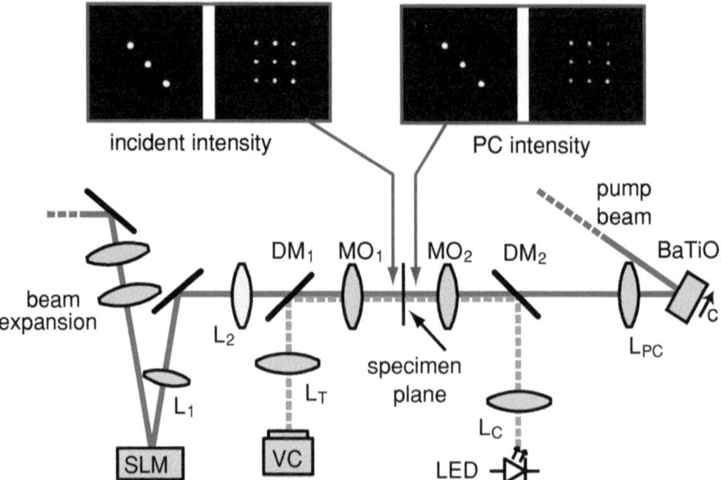

Fig. 4.9 Experimental setup for phase-conjugate counter-propagating traps using an SLM. The origin of trap and pump beams is omitted. *Insets* show two example trapping configurations as created with the SLM and measured in the specimen plane (*left*) and corresponding phase-conjugate replicas (*right*).

light field is phase-conjugated by the PCM. In this configuration the advantages of PC become even more evident than in the configurations with one or a few beams. The PCM inverts any arbitrary, complex wave front that is created by the SLM without the need for any precise adjustment. Hence, any configuration from a single up to hundreds of traps can be used; the respective CP antagonists are always built up automatically.

The calculation of the phase-patterns displayed on the SLM can be performed with many available algorithms. For the experiments discussed, a simple superposition of diffraction gratings and Fresnel lenses was utilised, which is easy to implement and fast in calculation (cf. Sect. 7.1.1). A few examples of possible trapping patterns are shown as insets in Fig. 4.9. The bright spots indicate the positions of the optical traps that are reflected from an air-glass interface (cover slip) of the sample. The corresponding back-propagating light field is generated by the PCM, propagates through the sample and is directly imaged onto the camera. Corresponding patterns overlap exactly, indicating the correct function of the PCM. Figure 4.10a shows an example of two particles that are trapped simultaneously. The left trap is positioned in focus, while the other trap is displaced in axial ($+z$) direction. Hence, the right particle is a few micrometers out of focus and barely visible. In Fig. 4.10b the situation is reversed: the left particle is displaced in axial ($-z$) direction, the other particle is in focus. This simple example clearly demonstrates the ability of the SLM based setup to trap and position multiple traps three dimensionally. Of course, more than two particles can be trapped simultaneously. Figures 4.10c–e show examples of multiple trapped particles. The trapping configuration can be changed by simply displaying

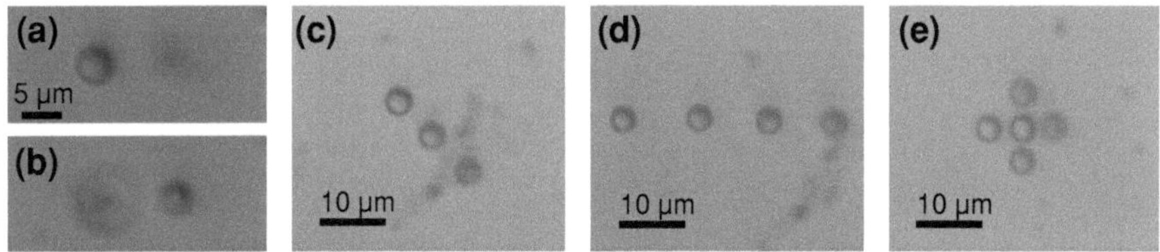

Fig. 4.10 Examples of trapping 4 μm beads with more complex configurations. **a, b** Two beads in different axial planes. **c–e** Increasing number of beads in various trapping configurations. From (Woerdemann et al. 2010).

a new phase-pattern on the SLM. After a time τ_{trap} trap which is directly related to the time constant of the PCM, τ, the new trapping configuration can be used.

Multiple optical traps reach their ultimate versatility if the traps—and thus the trapped particles—can be translated interactively and in real-time. It is obvious that the time constant τ of the PCM has a direct influence on the dynamics of the system. For many applications it is of interest how fast a particle with given properties can be moved from its initial position A to a destination B. Moving a particle with holographic optical traps always means a step-by-step motion, with a minimal step-size resulting from the SLM's pixilation. Consequently, there are two parameters that can be changed in order to increase the mean velocity: step-size and step-frequency. The diagram in Fig. 4.11 shows a study with a 4 μm particle for which both parameters were varied, using $P_T = 240\,\mu W$ of trap power and $P_P = 16\,mW$ for the pump beam. For each set of parameters, the probe particle was 10 times translated along the same trajectory from A to B with a length of $d = 10\,\mu m$, and it was recorded if the particle reached the final position or not. If the particle escaped from the trap during the motion, the translation was not successful. Parameter sets with 50% or more successful translations are considered suitable (black dots in the figure).

If only the time constant of the PCM were the limiting factor, the maximal steps per second should be independent from the step-size: it takes the PCM always the same time τ_{trap} to build up a new trap, independent from the distance between the old and the new trap. Figure 4.11, however, shows a clearly decreasing maximal step-frequency with increasing step-size. To gain insight into the reasons, we recall what happens when the position of a trap is changed. The old trap is switched off, the new trap is switched on; directly after switching, however, at the old trap's position there still is a back-propagating beam from the PCM. At the new position only the incident beam exists, but no CP antagonist. It takes a time τ_{trap} until the CP trap at the new position is established and the trap at the old position has vanished. During the reconfiguration, the incident beam at the new position and the back-propagating beam at the old position need to compensate for each other's scattering force. This works the more efficiently the closer the new trapping position is to the old position; hence, smaller step-sizes are favoured and allow for a higher step-frequency. This reasoning is supported by the observation that step-sizes larger than the particle diameter cannot be used at all.

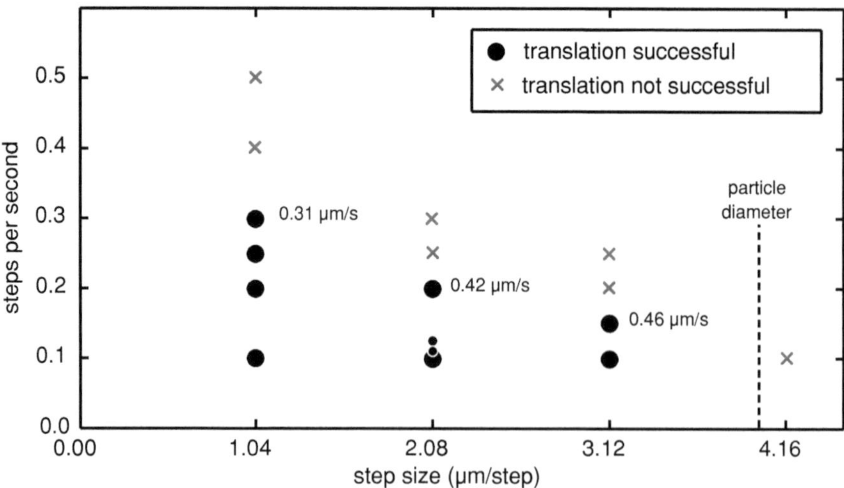

Fig. 4.11 A 4 µm polystyrene bead is translated with various step-sizes and step-frequencies. Each data point represents the majority vote of 10 single measurements (5 and 6 measurements for the small points, respectively). The maximal velocity is indicated for each step-size

With the intention to translate a given particle as fast as possible, therefore a larger step-size—but still below the particle diameter—is preferable. In the example, this choice makes it possible to move a 4 µm polystyrene bead with $v_{max} = (0.46 \pm 0.06)$ µm/s with a step-size of (3.12 ± 0.4) µm and 0.15 steps per second.

The time τ_{trap} it takes to build up a trap still is the limiting factor, once the step-size is chosen optimally. If τ_{trap} trap is given for some reason, the maximal velocity still can be increased if the trajectory is known in advance. With this knowledge, the next steps can be prepared by setting up a few traps along the trajectory, just in front of the particle. These traps have time to fully establish CP traps. In order to translate the particle, the trap on the particle's old position and the trap directly behind that position are switched off. The particle will take one step. With this approach of "paving the way", utilising 5 traps ($P_T = 670$ µW total), it was possible to move a 4 µm particle with a velocity up to $v_{max} = (2.72 \pm 0.88)$ µm/s. The achievable velocity is thus significantly higher than in the single trap mode, although the used power per trap is less than half.

4.5 Conclusion and Perspectives

The resulting system is somewhat complex from the physical point of view. It is, for example, not trivial and highly interesting how the particle interacts with the light field. In the case of an infinitesimally small particle, we can safely assume that the incident light field is unaltered and reflected by the PCM as illustrated in Fig. 4.4b.

A particle of a few micrometers on the other hand certainly does interact with the incident light field by scattering. Possible consequences are that not all scattered light might be recollected after passing through the particle and the light field that reaches the PCM is additionally modified, e. g. by focusing effects of the particle. Furthermore, the particle is not still, even if it is not translated intentionally, but vibrates in the trap because of Brownian motion. The power spectrum of this vibration (depending on the trap stiffness and temperature; cf. Sect. 2.5) yields characteristic time constants τ_{vib} that can be compared to τ. In the discussed implementation, the PCM has time constants τ in the order of seconds which is very large compared to typical values of τ_{vib}. Hence, the PCM reflects an averaged light field.

The response time of the PCM also limits the maximal possible velocity with which a particle can be translated. With the current setup, velocities up to about $3\,\mu\mathrm{m/s}$ are accessible. The chosen photorefractive implementation of a PCM is not only known for its high fidelity and the low required light intensities, but also has a very long response time compared to most other ways to realise optical PC (He 2002). It thus should be easy to decrease the time constant τ by many orders of magnitude. Then, the PCM is no longer the limiting factor in translation speed, but other factors, like the available optical force and the viscosity of the medium that surrounds the particle become dominant.

Many applications of optical traps involve the trapping of biological cells. The demonstrated setup uses green ($\lambda = 532\,\mathrm{nm}$) light, which is a good choice for the manipulation of artificial objects, but causes serious photodamage in living cells. Better suited wavelengths are in the near infrared (NIR), with 830 and 970 nm being optimal in many cases (Neuman et al. 1999). It should be straightforward to extend the presented concept to NIR wavelengths, as there are photorefractive materials available that provide high reflectivity in this wavelength regime (e. g. cobalt-doped $BaTiO_3$ (Rytz et al. 1990)).

In summary, it was demonstrated that CP optical traps which utilise optical PC can be a versatile tool in optical micromanipulation. On the one hand, they inherit most desired features, in particular low possible numerical apertures and thus high working distances, increased axial symmetry of the optical potentials and reduced intensities compared to single beam optical tweezers. On the other hand, they are self-aligning and adapt automatically to any arbitrary input trap configuration. The basic concept of a single CP trap has been developed towards multiple, dynamic traps, paving the way towards advanced applications. The dynamic capabilities include reconfigurable traps and three-dimensional translation of the trapped particles in real-time. Having demonstrated that SLMs can be used with PC optical traps, it is possible to use almost any complex, structured light field as the basis for novel trapping configurations. Exciting examples are interference patterns of multiple plane waves (Schonbrun et al. 2005, Xavier et al. 2010), vortex beams that carry orbital angular momentum (Woerdemann et al. 2009), higher order self-similar beams (cf. Chap. 6), or non-diffracting beams (cf. Chap. 5).

References

Ashkin A (1970) Acceleration and trapping of particles by radiation pressure. Phys Rev Lett 24:156–159

Ashkin A (2000) History of optical trapping and manipulation of small-neutral particle, atoms, and molecules. IEEE J Sel Top Quantum Electron 6:841–856

Ashkin A, Dziedzic J (1985) Observation of radiation-pressure trapping of particles by alternating light-beams. Phys Rev Lett 54:1245–1248

Ashkin A, Dziedzic J, Bjorkholm J, Chu S (1986) Observation of a single-beam gradient force optical trap for dielectric particles. Opt Lett 11:288–290

Berghoff K (2010) Erzeugung von Mehrfachfallen und komplexen Fanggeometrien in dynamischen phasenkonjugierten gegenläufigen optischen Fallen. Master's thesis, Westfälische Wilhelms-Universität Münster

Born M, Wolf E (1986) Principles of optics. Pergamon Press, Oxford

Bowman R, Jesacher A, Thalhammer G, Gibson G, Ritsch-Marte M, Padgett M (2011) Position clamping in a holographic counterpropagating optical trap. Opt Express 19:9908–9914

Boyd R (1992) Nonlinear optics. Academic, San Diego

Chiou A (1999) Photorefractive phase-conjugate optics for image processing, trapping, and manipulation of microscopic objects. IEEE Proc 87:2074–2085

Constable A, Kim J, Mervis J, Zarinetchi F, Prentiss M (1993) Demonstration of a fiber-optical light-force trap. Opt Lett 18:1867–1869

Croningolomb M (1991) Nonlinear optics and phase conjugation in photorefractive materials. J Cryst Growth 109:345–352

Dam J, Rodrigo P, Perch-Nielsen I, Alonzo C, Glückstad J (2007a) Computerized "drag-and-drop" alignment of GPC-based optical micromanipulation system. Opt Express 15:1923–1931

Dam J, Rodrigo P, Perch-Nielsen I, Glückstad J (2007b) Fully automated beam-alignment and single stroke guided manual alignment of counter-propagating multi-beam based optical micro-manipulation systems. Opt Express 15:7968–7973

Dholakia K, Reece P (2006) Optical micromanipulation takes hold. Nano Today 1:18–27

Feinberg J (1982) Self-pumped, continuous-wave phase conjugator using internal-reflection. Opt Lett 7:486–488

Feinberg J (1983) Continuous-wave self-pumped phase conjugator with wide field of view. Opt Lett 8:480–482

Feinberg J, Hellwarth R (1980) Phase-conjugating mirror with continuous-wave gain. Opt Lett 5:519–521

Fisher R (ed) (1983) Optical phase conjugation. Academic, New York

Guck J, Ananthakrishnan R, Cunningham CC, Käs J (2002) Stretching biological cells with light. J Phys Condens Matter 14:4843–4856

He G (2002) Optical phase conjugation: principles, techniques, and applications. Prog Quantum Electron 26:131–191

Hellwarth R (1977) Generation of time-reversed wave fronts by nonlinear refraction. J Opt Soc Am 67:1–3

Hörner F, Woerdemann M, Müller S, Maier B, Denz C (2010) Full 3D translational and rotational optical control of multiple rod-shaped bacteria. J Biophotonics 3:468–475

Jonas A, Zemanek P (2008) Light at work: the use of optical forces for particle manipulation, sorting, and analysis. Electrophoresis 29:4813–4851

Martin-Badosa E, Montes-Usategui M, Carnicer A, Andilla J, Pleguezuelos E, Juvells I (2007) Design strategies for optimizing holographic optical tweezers set-ups. J Opt A: Pure Appl Opt 9:S267–S277

Neuman K, Block S (2004) Optical trapping. Rev Sci Instrum 75:2787–2809

Neuman K, Chadd E, Liou G, Bergman K, Block S (1999) Characterization of photodamage to Escherichia coli in optical traps. Biophys J 77:2856–2863

Petrovic M, Beli M, Denz C, Kivshar Y (2011) Counterpropagating optical beams and solitons. Laser Photonics Rev 5:214–233

Rodrigo P, Daria V, Gluckstad J (2005) Four-dimensional optical manipulation of colloidal particles. Appl Phys Lett 86:074103

Rodrigo P, Perch-Nielsen I, Glückstad J (2006) Three-dimensional forces in GPC-based counterpropagating-beam traps. Opt Express 14:5812–5822

Rytz D, Stephens R, Wechsler B, Keirstead M, Baer T (1990) Efficient self-pumped phase conjugation at near-infrared wavelengths using Cobalt-doped $BaTiO_3$. Opt Lett 15:1279–1281

Schonbrun E, Piestun R, Jordan P, Cooper J, Wulff K, Courtial J, Padgett M (2005) 3D interferometric optical tweezers using a single spatial light modulator. Opt Express 13:3777–3786

Sinclair G, Jordan P, Leach J, Padgett M, Cooper J (2004) Defining the trapping limits of holographical optical tweezers. J Mod Opt 51:409–414

Svoboda K, Block SM (1994) Biological applications of optical forces. Annu Rev Biophys Biomol Struct 23:247–285

Tauro S, Banas A, Palima D, Glückstad J (2010) Dynamic axial stabilization of counter-propagating beam-traps with feedback control. Opt Express 18:18217–18222

Thalhammer G, Steiger R, Bernet S, Ritsch-Marte M (2011) Optical macro-tweezers: trapping of highly motile micro-organisms. J Opt 13:044024

Wang W, Chiou A, Sonek G, Berns M (1997) Self-aligned dual-beam optical laser trap using photorefractive phase conjugation. J Opt Soc Am B 14:697–704

Woerdemann M, Alpmann C, Denz C (2009) Self-pumped phase conjugation of light beams carrying orbital angular momentum. Opt Express 17:22791–22799

Woerdemann M, Berghoff K, Denz C (2010) Dynamic multiple-beam counter-propagating optical traps using optical phase-conjugation. Opt Express 18:22348–57

Woerdemann M, Gläsener S, Hörner F, Devaux A, De Cola L, Denz C (2010) Dynamic and reversible organization of zeolite L crystals induced by holographic optical tweezers. Adv Mater 22:4176–4179

Xavier J, Boguslawski M, Rose P, Joseph J, Denz C (2010) Reconfigurable optically induced quasicrystallographic three-dimensional complex nonlinear photonic lattice structures. Adv Mater 22:356

Xie P, Dai J, Wang P, Zhang H (1997) Self-pumped phase conjugation in photorefractive crystals: reflectivity and spatial fidelity. Phys Rev A 55:3092–3100

Yeh P (1993) Introduction to photorefractive nonlinear optics. Wiley, New York

Zemanek P, Jonas A, Sramek L, Liska M (1998) Optical trapping of Rayleigh particles using a Gaussian standing wave. Opt Commun 151:273–285

Zemanek P, Jonas A, Sramek L, Liska M (1999) Optical trapping of nanoparticles and microparticles by a Gaussian standing wave. Opt Lett 24:1448–1450

Zemanek P, Jonas A, Liska M (2002) Simplified description of optical forces acting on a nanoparticle in the Gaussian standing wave. J Opt Soc Am A 19:1025–1034

Zemanek P, Jonas A, Jakl P, Jezek J, Sery M, Liska M (2003) Theoretical comparison of optical traps created by standing wave and single beam. Opt Commun 220:401–412

Zozulya A (1993) Fanning and photorefractive self-pumped four-wave mixing geometries. IEEE J Quantum Electron 29:538 555

Zwick S, Haist T, Miyamoto Y, He L, Warber M, Hermerschmidt A, Osten W (2009) Holographic twin traps. J Opt A: Pure Appl Opt 11:034011

Chapter 5
Non-Diffracting Beams for the Three-Dimensional Moulding of Matter

The class of propagation-invariant light fields or non-diffracting beams features the unique property of a transverse beam profile that does not alter during propagation. This behaviour is in strong contrast to other light fields, including Gaussian beams or complex light fields in holographic optical tweezers, that inevitably spread during propagation and hence restrict optical micromanipulation to the vicinity of the focal plane. In particular with high numerical aperture microscope objectives, which are essential for diffraction limited microscopic observation, the tight focusing results in strong spreading and short axial extension of optical trapping landscapes. Experimental approximations of ideal non-diffracting beams can yield significantly extended axial potential wells. Furthermore, they are self-reconstructing in a sense that the light field can re-establish itself after being obstructed by a small obstacle. After a short introduction into general non-diffracting beams, this chapter focuses on Mathieu beams, a fundamental class of solutions of the Helmholtz equation in elliptical coordinates. Besides their propagation-invariant properties, Mathieu beams feature a wide range of different transverse field distributions that can be selected according to experimental requirements. It is shown that Mathieu beams can provide optical trapping landscapes that enable moulding extended three-dimensional structures of spherical and non-spherical microscopic particles.

5.1 What is a Non-Diffracting Beam?

Every localised light field undergoes diffraction, even during free-space propagation, resulting in changes of the transverse profile. A well known example is the fundamental Gaussian beam, or TEM_{00} laser mode, that can be collimated only for a certain distance, usually defined as two time the Rayleigh length,[1] and unavoidably spreads on further propagation. There are, however, examples of light fields that apparently behave differently. An ideal plane wave, with infinite transverse

---

[1] The Rayleigh length is given by $z_R = \pi\omega_0^2/\lambda$, with the beam waist ω_0 of the lowest order Gaussian beam.

M. Woerdemann, *Structured Light Fields*, Springer Theses, DOI: 10.1007/978-3-642-29323-8_5, © Springer-Verlag Berlin Heidelberg 2012

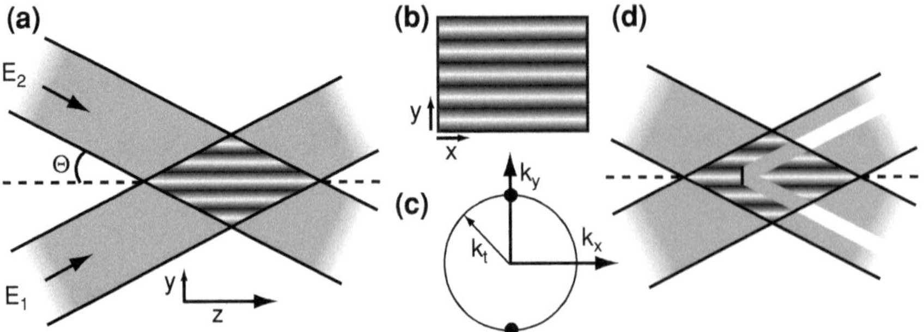

Fig. 5.1 The interference pattern of two plane waves (**a**) can be interpreted as propagation-invariant light field with transverse cosine grating (**b**), which consists of two discrete spatial frequencies (**c**). After a small obstacle, the original transverse intensity distribution is reconstructed in propagation direction (**d**)

extension, by definition does not alter during propagation. The simplest, nontrivial, example of a propagation-invariant light field is the interference of two plane waves that enclose angles $\pm\Theta$ with the propagation direction z as depicted in Fig. 5.1a. This light field features a sinusoidal transverse intensity profile and already shows two important features of the class of *non-diffracting* beams. First, the transverse intensity (Fig. 5.1b) is propagation-invariant for the ideal case of infinite constituting plane waves and second, it has self-healing or *self-reconstructing* properties as visualised in Fig. 5.1d. Self-reconstructing means that the light field re-establishes its transverse intensity profile after being disturbed by a (small) obstacle. For many applications a transverse localisation of the propagation-invariant light field—rather than a spatially extended transverse field distribution—is favourable, leading to the actual concept of non-diffracting *beams*.

For a more systematic approach, we consider the Helmholtz equation

$$\nabla^2 E + \frac{\omega^2}{c^2} E = 0. \tag{5.1}$$

A propagation-invariant solution $E(x, y, z)$ would have to be separable into a transverse function that only depends on transverse coordinates and a longitudinal function that only depends on the propagation direction z (Turunen and Friberg 2010):[2]

$$E(x, y, z) = V(x, y)e^{ik_z z}. \tag{5.2}$$

Obviously, this solution would result in a transverse intensity pattern $I(x, y, z) = |E(x, y, z)|^2 = I(x, y, 0)$ that does not change during propagation.

This ansatz yields solutions in four coordinate systems. The fundamental families of solutions are plane waves in Cartesian coordinates, Bessel beams in circular cylindrical coordinates, Mathieu beams in elliptic cylindrical coordinates, and parabolic

---

[2] Here, the axial wave vector k_z is introduced which is related to the wave vector k and the transverse wave vector k_t by $k^2 = k_z^2 + k_t^2$.

(or Weber) beams in parabolic cylindrical coordinates (Gutierrez-Vega and Bandres 2005). Each fundamental family is a basis for expanding any non-diffracting beam with the same transverse spatial frequency k_t. In particular, using Whittaker's integral (Mazilu et al. 2009)

$$V(x, y) = \int_0^{2\pi} A(\phi) \exp\left[-ik_t \left(x \cos(\phi) + y \sin(\phi)\right)\right] d\phi \tag{5.3}$$

a general solution for non-diffracting beams can be given in terms of plane waves, where $A(\phi)$ is an arbitrary, complex function. Thus, any non-diffracting beam can be represented by a superposition of plane waves whose wave vectors lie on an infinitesimally narrow ring in the Fourier plane, defined by k_t (cf. Fig. 5.1c).

5.2 Experimental Approximations of Non-Diffracting Beams

Obviously, neither infinitely extended plane waves nor an infinitesimally narrow ring in the Fourier plane can be realised experimentally. The first would require infinite energy and infinitely large apertures, the latter would imply infinite intensity on the ring for non-diffracting wave fields with non-zero energy. However, it is possible to generate experimental approximations to ideal non-diffracting beams that can be considered propagation-invariant over a certain, finite, non-diffracting length.

The first study on non-diffracting beams proposed a simple choice $A(\phi) \equiv 1$, resulting in a transverse beam profile of

$$V(x, y) = \int_0^{2\pi} \exp\left[-ik_t \left(x \cos(\phi) + y \sin(\phi)\right)\right] d\phi = J_0(k_t r), \tag{5.4}$$

the zeroth order Bessel function of the first kind (Durnin 1987). This Bessel beam can be generated with a conical lens or *axicon* (McLeod 1954) of radius R, which is illuminated with a plane wave. For this case, the length $2z_{\max}$ over which the non-diffracting beam exists can be estimated with simple geometric arguments (Durnin 1987):

$$2z_{\max} = R \sqrt{\left(\left(\frac{2\pi}{k_t \lambda}\right)^2 - 1\right)}. \tag{5.5}$$

The same estimation holds true for all non-diffracting beams as defined by Eq. (5.3) if the aperture of the constituting plane waves is defined equivalently to the Bessel beam created by an axicon.

A more realistic description of experimental approximations to non-diffracting beams can be achieved when considering an ideal non-diffracting beam, apodised at the plane $z = 0$ with a Gaussian envelope:

$$V_{\text{HG}}(x, y, z = 0) = V_{\text{HG}}(r, \phi, z = 0) = V(x, y)\mathrm{e}^{-r^2/\omega_0^2}. \qquad (5.6)$$

It can be shown that this is equivalent to all plane waves constituting the non-diffracting beam having a Gaussian shape (Gori et al. 1987) and yielding an annular ring in the Fourier plane with a finite width of $4/\omega_0$ (Gutierrez-Vega and Bandres 2005). With this assumption, the beam can be estimated to be a good approximation of a non-diffracting beam for $-z_{\text{max,GB}} \leq z \leq +z_{\text{max,GB}}$ with (Gutierrez-Vega and Bandres 2005)

$$z_{\text{max,GB}} = 2z_R/k_t\omega_0. \qquad (5.7)$$

This estimation is valid if the divergence angle Θ_G of the constituting Gaussian beams is much smaller than the half-aperture angle Θ_0 of the cone on which these waves propagate: $\gamma = \Theta_0/\Theta_G \gg 1$ (Gori et al. 1987). The Gaussian envelope approximations to ideal non-diffracting beams are known as *Helmholtz-Gauss* beams (Gutierrez-Vega and Bandres 2005), in particular Bessel-Gauss beams (Gori et al. 1987), Mathieu-Gauss beams, etc.

While experimental approximations to the initial example of two interfering plane waves can be easily realised with two discrete beams and lowest order Bessel beams can be generated either with a refractive axicon (McLeod 1954, Scott and McArdle 1992), or a circular slit in a Fourier plane (Durnin et al. 1987), general non-diffracting beams cannot be generated with a simple optical element. There are two ways to tailor an arbitrary non-diffracting beam; an incident laser beam can be modulated directly, or the Fourier plane, i. e. the angular spectrum of the non-diffracting beam, can be modulated. In both cases, the actual modulation can be performed with computer-generated holograms in the form of diffractive optical elements (DOEs). In general, the desired non-diffracting beam has a complex transverse field distribution $V(x, y)$ as well as a complex annular angular spectrum $A(\phi)$, requiring complex valued modulation through the DOE. While there are (static) DOEs that can modulate amplitude and phase of a wave front simultaneously, there are no computer-addressable spatial light modulators (SLMs) available that can perform complex valued modulation (Zwick et al. 2010). To achieve the best diffraction efficiency, hence, usually phase-only SLMs are employed as DOEs if the versatility of reconfigurable, dynamic generation of non-diffracting beams is desired. Phase-only DOEs cannot directly modulate the amplitude of an incident light field, but nevertheless amplitude information can be encoded indirectly (Davis et al. 1999). In a simplified picture, the phase-only hologram that encodes the phase Ψ of a wave $\hat{U}(x, y) = |\hat{U}(x, y)|\exp(-i\Psi(x, y))$ is multiplied with a spatial carrier frequency grating. The diffraction efficiency of the DOE then is modulated locally in order to emulate the amplitude $|\hat{U}(x, y)|$. A more rigorous treatment of complex modulation with phase-only SLMs is provided in Appendix A.

From the experimental point of view, direct modulation of the incident laser beam is relatively straight-forward when the (complex) transverse field distribution

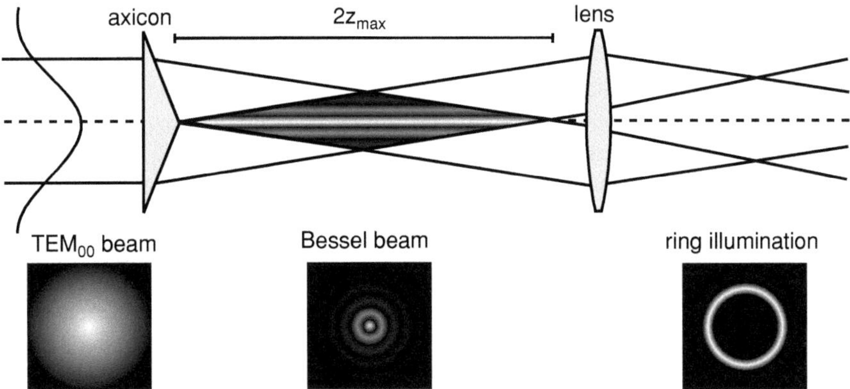

Fig. 5.2 Conversion of a Gaussian TEM$_{00}$ beam into a Bessel(-Gauss) beam by an axicon lens (*left part*) and subsequent optical Fourier transformation of the Bessel beam (*right part*). The light ring can be interpreted as the angular spectrum of the Bessel beam ($A(\phi) \equiv 1$). Also, it can serve as a *ring-shaped* illumination of a DOE for efficient creation of non-diffracting beams in the Fourier plane (see text for details)

is known. By this means, holographic generation of a wide range of different non-diffracting beams was demonstrated. Examples are the generation of lowest order Bessel beams by means of a holographic axicon (Turunen et al. 1988, Davis et al. 1993), higher order Bessel beams (Vasara et al. 1989), Mathieu beams (Chavez-Cerda et al. 2002), or superpositions of discrete numbers of plane waves (Boguslawski et al. 2011). Modulation of the angular spectrum requires a more sophisticated approach as the complete light field is confined on a narrow ring in the Fourier plane. If a DOE is illuminated with a plane wave or an expanded Gaussian wave, the diffraction efficiency is extremely low, since the ring only occupies a small fraction of the active area of the DOE. An ingenious solution to this problem is pre-shaping the incident light field with either a refractive or a diffractive axicon (Alpmann et al. 2010, Lautanen et al. 2000) and a positive lens into a narrow ring (Bélanger and Rioux 1978). By these means, diffraction efficiency is dramatically increased as all available laser light power is already confined on a ring and the SLM only needs to introduce the complex function $A(\phi)$. Figure 5.2 shows the basic configuration of an axicon and a positive lens that can be utilised to convert a fundamental Gaussian beam into a Bessel-Gauss beam and subsequently into a ring-shaped intensity distribution. The ring of intensity represents the angular spectrum of the Bessel-Gauss beam and can be used as the pre-shaped illumination of a DOE generating a non-diffracting beam in the Fourier plane.

5.3 Non-Diffracting Beams as Optical Traps

Non-diffracting beams have (at least) three outstanding properties that make them highly interesting for optical trapping applications. First, their propagation-invariant property allows for an extended area of optical manipulation along the beam axis compared to, for example, Gaussian beams commonly used in optical tweezers. This means optical manipulation can take place deep inside a sample, through thick (transparent) obstacles, or in multiple planes. Second, non-diffracting beams are self-reconstructing, i. e. their transverse field distribution is reconstructed after small disturbances. This can be advantageous if the beam path to the manipulated object is not free space but contains obstacles like impurities or other absorbing or scattering objects, or if the optical manipulation of multiple objects along the beam axis is desired. Finally, owing to the fact that $A(\phi)$ can be any arbitrary complex function, non-diffracting beams feature a wealth of transverse intensity distributions ranging from the well-known concentric ring system of the Bessel beam over highly periodic or quasiperiodic discrete patterns (Boguslawski et al. 2011) to apparently random, speckle-like intensity patterns (Turunen et al. 1991). The diversity in intensity patterns directly translates into a similar diversity of possible optical potential landscapes.

These unique properties have led to several exciting applications in optical trapping. The first demonstration that optical trapping with non-diffracting beams is possible was published a decade ago (Arlt et al. 2001). In this seminal study, a zeroth order Bessel beam was utilised to trap several microspheres along the central maximum of the Bessel beam and thus produce a stack of spheres. Later, it was shown that a Bessel beam can even be used for optical manipulation in two different sample chambers that are separated by a macroscopic distance (Garcès-Chàvez et al. 2002). The long available distance of several Rayleigh lengths of a comparable Gaussian beam was only possible because the Bessel beam is propagation-invariant, while the simultaneous operation in two sample chambers along the beam axis was enabled by its self-reconstruction after being disturbed in the first chamber.

The transverse field distribution of a Bessel beam cannot only be used to confine particles on the intensity rings (Garcès-Chàvez et al. 2002), but it also serves as an experimental realisation of an optical concentric washboard type potential that is an ideal platform for studying Brownian dynamics (Tatarkova et al. 2003). Furthermore, it can be applied to collect particles from a wide area and guide them to the centre by utilising the asymmetry of the potential landscape. Higher order Bessel beams also feature optical vortices that can transfer optical orbital angular momentum to particles (Volke-Sepulveda et al. 2004). Owing to the radially alternating intensity distribution, not only transparent high-index[3] particles can be confined and set into continuous rotation on a circle around the beam axis (Volke-Sepulveda et al. 2002), but also orbital angular momentum can be transferred to absorbing particles and low-index particles that are confined on a ring of minimal intensity (Garces-Chavez et al. 2002). The rotation of particles on Bessel beam rings with different radii enables

---

3 High-index particles are particles with a refractive index higher than the surrounding medium.

a thorough experimental investigation on intrinsic and extrinsic nature of orbital angular momentum (Garces-Chavez et al. 2003, O'Neil et al. 2002).

More advanced applications require more complex optical potential landscapes than a Bessel beam can provide (McGloin and Dholakia 2005). One obvious extension is using a superposition of multiple Bessel beams. The interference pattern of multiple non-diffracting beams retains the non-diffracting property and, for example, enable optical manipulation on circular spot arrays (McGloin and Dholakia 2005). Furthermore, fundamental solutions of the Helmholtz equation other than the Bessel beam could be utilised. Recently, Airy beams[4] were generated with an SLM and used to guide particles along a curved trajectory. Also *helical* Mathieu beams have been utilised in optical micromanipulation (Lopez-Mariscal et al. 2006). Helical Mathieu beams are a particular subset of the general class of Mathieu beams that are introduced in the following section. At this point, the helical Mathieu beams utilised in optical micromanipulation can be imagined as elliptical doughnut beams that accelerate particles along an ellipsis rather than a circle compared to a common (Laguerre-Gaussian) doughnut beam (He et al. 1995) (cf. also Sect. 2.8).

In summary, it can be stated that non-diffracting beams have a high potential for applications in optical micromanipulation. Most experimental demonstrations so far were restricted to simple Bessel beams with a few promising exceptions. There is a strong demand for new experimental schemes that can only be realised with the emergence of advanced beam-shaping concepts in recent years.

5.4 Moulding Matter with Mathieu Beams

Holographic optical tweezers are powerful tools for assembling microscopic particles one by one into highly complex three-dimensional structures. A complementary approach with different strengths and limitation is the preparation of an appropriate optical potential landscape, or *light mould*, that guides the self-assembly of multiple particles into defined amalgamations. While basic examples for guided self-assembly of microspheres in the concentric optical potential well of Bessel beams have been demonstrated (McGloin and Dholakia 2005), it is clear that more sophisticated structures require more flexibility with respect to the transverse intensity distribution of the light field. The propagation-invariant and self-reconstructing properties of non-diffracting beams are very advantageous for the optical moulding of matter as they enable an extension of the structure in the direction of beam propagation.

---

[4] Airy beams cannot be understood in the strict description of propagation-invariant wave fields and in particular do not obey Eq. (5.2). Sometimes Airy beams are conceived as a "second type of non-diffracting beam" (Baumgartl et al. 2008) which is termed *accelerating* non-diffracting beams in contrast to the *straight* non-diffracting beams discussed in this chapter.

5.4.1 Mathieu Beams

Mathieu beams meet all demands as they are the fundamental class of non-diffracting solutions of the Helmholtz equation in elliptical coordinates. Since eccentricity is a free parameter, transverse intensity patterns with a wide range of symmetries can be selected, including polar and Cartesian beams.

The elliptical coordinates (ξ, η) are given by

$$\xi = \mathfrak{Re}(\operatorname{arccosh}((x + iy)/f)) \tag{5.8}$$

$$\eta = \mathfrak{Im}(\operatorname{arccosh}((x + iy)/f)), \tag{5.9}$$

with the eccentricity parameter f. In these coordinates, the solutions of the Helmholtz equation can be separated in a transverse and a longitudinal function as described by Eq. (5.2). Solutions to the transverse part again separate into an angular and a radial part that obey the angular and radial Mathieu equations (Gutierrez-Vega et al. 2000). Both equations can be reduced to the *Mathieu equation* with the substitution $\eta = i\xi$:

$$\left[\frac{\partial^2}{\partial u^2} + (a - 2q \cos(2u)) \right] W(u) = 0, \tag{5.10}$$

where a is the separation constant and $q = f^2 k_t^2/4$ gives the ellipticity of the solutions. Due to the nature of the differential equation, two solutions are obtained (Arscott 1964) that yield the *odd* and *even* solutions for the transverse Helmholtz equation in elliptical coordinates, the odd $(M_m^o(\eta, \xi, q))$ and even $(M_m^e(\eta, \xi, q))$ Mathieu beams (Gutierrez-Vega and Bandres 2005):

$$M_m^e(\eta, \xi, q) = C_m Je_m(\xi, q)\, ce_m(\eta, q) \qquad m = 0, 1, 2, 3\ldots \tag{5.11}$$

$$M_m^o(\eta, \xi, q) = S_m Jo_m(\xi, q)\, se_m(\eta, q) \qquad m = 1, 2, 3.\ldots \tag{5.12}$$

Here, $Je_m(\xi, q)$ and $Jo_m(\xi, q)$ are the even and odd modified Mathieu functions of order m, and $ce_m(\eta, q)$ and $se_m(\eta, q)$ are the even and odd ordinary Mathieu functions of order m, and C_m and S_m are constant. Details on the numerical calculation of the Mathieu functions are provided in Appendix B.1. Figures 5.3 and 5.4 show a selection of different even and odd Mathieu beams, indicating their transverse intensity and phase distribution in the near-field and far-field.

Besides even and odd Mathieu beams, also a superposition of both, known as *helical* Mathieu beams can be considered:

$$HM_m^{\pm}(\eta, \xi, q) = M_m^e(\eta, \xi, q) \pm iM_m^o(\eta, \xi, q) \qquad m = 1, 2, 3\ldots \tag{5.13}$$

Helical Mathieu beams show point singularities and helical phase front features, or optical vortices (Chavez-Cerda et al. 2001). These properties can be highly interesting in optical micromanipulation as optical vortices carry orbital angular momentum. With Bessel beams and Laguerre-Gaussian modes, transfer of orbital angular

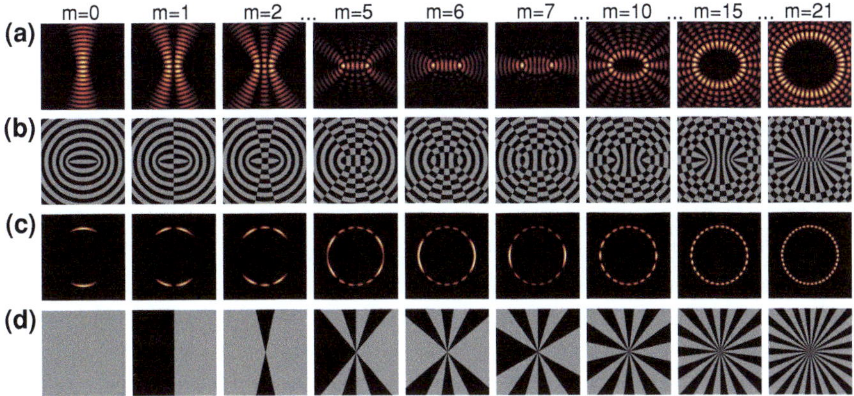

Fig. 5.3 Selection of even Mathieu beams of order m. **a** Transverse intensity distribution of the non-diffracting beam, calculated as $|\mathrm{M}_m^e(\eta, \xi, q)|^2$ from Eq. (5.11); intensity is normalised and depicted in false colour for better visibility. **b** Corresponding phase distribution $\mathfrak{Im}\left(\log \mathrm{M}_m^e(\eta, \xi, q)\right)$. The *bright* and *dark grey* values correspond to a phase of 0 and π, respectively. **c** In a Fourier plane, intensity is confined to a narrow ring. **d** Phase distribution in the Fourier plane

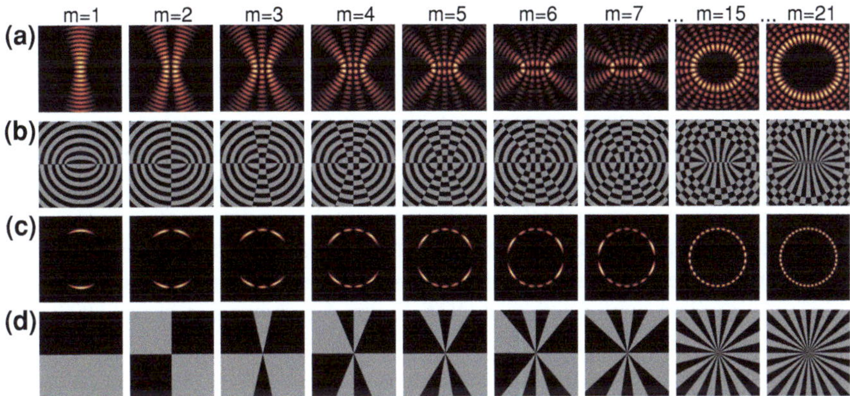

Fig. 5.4 Selection of odd Mathieu beams of order m. **a** Transverse intensity distribution of the non-diffracting beam, calculated as $|\mathrm{M}_m^o(\eta, \xi, q)|^2$ from Eq. (5.12); intensity is normalised and depicted in false colour for better visibility. **b** Corresponding phase distribution $\mathfrak{Im}\left(\log \mathrm{M}_m^o(\eta, \xi, q)\right)$. The *bright* and *dark grey* values correspond to a phase of 0 and π, respectively. **c** In a Fourier plane, intensity is confined to a narrow ring. **d** Phase distribution in the Fourier plane

momentum to particles has been investigated in depth (Volke-Sepulveda et al. 2004). While those wave fields have relatively simple circular geometries, in particular the lower order helical Mathieu beams (cf. Fig. 5.5) feature complex intensity distributions combined with multiple, highly ordered optical vortices. So far, however, only the higher order helical Mathieu beams with their sober intensity distribution in the shape of concentric ellipsis have been employed in optical micromanipulation (Lopez-Mariscal et al. 2006).

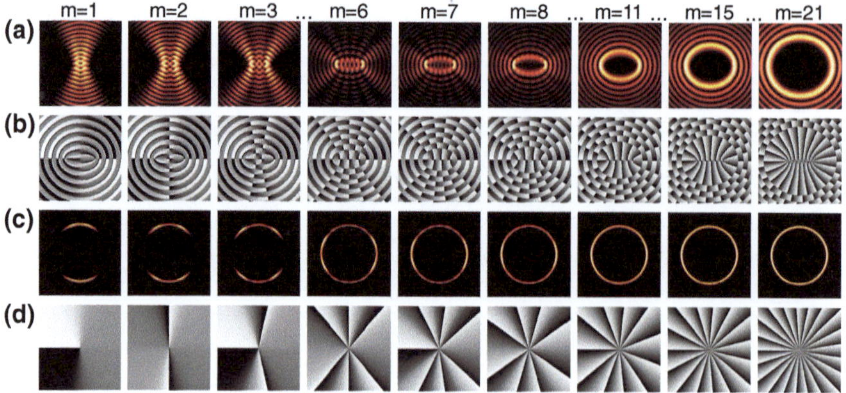

Fig. 5.5 Selection of helical Mathieu beams of order m. **a** Transverse intensity distribution of the non-diffracting beam, calculated as $|\text{HM}_m^{\pm}(\eta, \xi, q)|^2$ from Eq. (5.13); intensity is normalised and depicted in false colour for better visibility. **b** Corresponding phase distribution $\Im\left(\log \text{HM}_m^{\pm}(\eta, \xi, q)\right)$. The *grey* values correspond to a phase interval of 0 to 2π. **c** In a Fourier plane, intensity is confined to a narrow ring. **d** Phase distribution in the Fourier plane

5.4.2 Experimental Schemes

In order to demonstrate the potential of Mathieu beams in optical micromanipulation and in particular in optical moulding of matter, two distinct experiments have been developed. One general design constraint was that the Mathieu beams can be integrated into conventional HOT without a complete redesign of the setup. This goal is achieved if the holographic generation of the Mathieu beams is performed in a Fourier plane with respect to the observation plane of the microscope because this is the standard configuration in HOT. Figure 5.6 shows a modified HOT setup that utilises pre-shaped illumination as described above (cf. Fig. 5.2) for the efficient generation of non-diffracting beams in general and Mathieu beams in particular. Basically, an axicon and a positive lens are introduced before the SLM, such that the SLM is illuminated by a narrow ring of light and consequently can modulate $A(\phi)$ with high efficiency. The SLM modulates the complex transverse light field according to the numerical values found for an either even or odd Mathieu beam of order m with the desired eccentricity as calculated from Eqs. (5.11) and (5.12). Details on the actual encoding of phase and amplitude information on the (phase-only) SLM are discussed in Appendix A.

The first experiment should clearly demonstrate that the transverse intensity distribution of an even or odd Mathieu beam can be utilised to arrange particles in the transverse plane, thereby transferring the high degree of spatial order to the particle structure. At the same time, the non-diffracting property should be exploited in the sense that the created particle assembly is extended in the third dimension along the beam axis. Figure 5.7 shows the intensity distributions of an even 7th order Mathieu beam in the transverse $x - y$ plane and in a $x - z$ plane containing the optical axis.

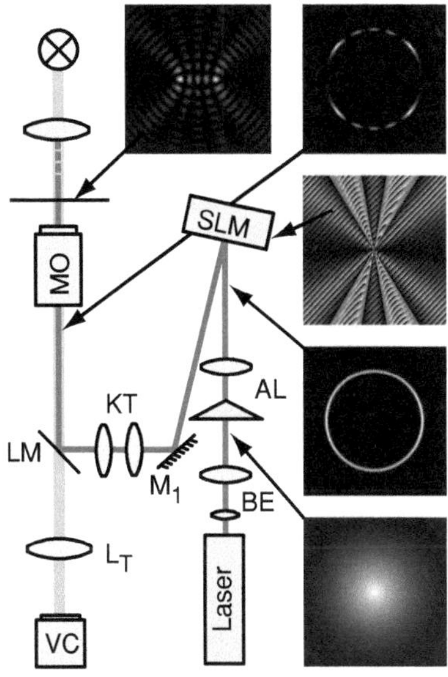

Fig. 5.6 Principle setup for the generation of general non-diffracting and in particular Mathieu beams for optical micromanipulation. *BE* beam expansion; *AL* axicon and lens; M_1 relay mirror; *KT* relay telescope; *LM* laser line mirror; L_T tube lens; *MO* microscope objective; *VC* video camera

According to the general theory of light-matter interaction (cf. Chap. 2), micron-sized transparent particles are expected to be attracted by the intensity maxima with a force that is proportional to the local intensity gradient. Furthermore, due to the lack of axial intensity gradients, the scattering force is expected to push the particles in the direction of beam propagation. This is avoided by choosing microspheres of silica dispersed in water that show significant sedimentation. The power of the laser is set to a value that exactly compensates for the gravitational forces and thus enables stable three-dimensional trapping of the microspheres. With this configuration it should be possible to create a three-dimensional, double-chain like structure that is confined to the two intensity maxima of the transverse beam profile and extended in axial direction. The maximal length of the chains depends on several parameters, including the length z_{max} of the non-diffracting beam, the interaction time and density of particles.

The second experiment is supposed to make direct use of the eccentricity of the transverse optical potential landscape. Therefore, elongated silica particles are employed that usually align themselves with the optical axis in optical tweezers. An in-depth discussion of this problem is given in Sect. 7.3, but at this point it is sufficient to understand that horizontal alignment of elongated particles is a non-trivial and important task for many applications. The idea is to employ the transverse eccentricity of Mathieu beams to align elongated objects in the transverse plane. Owing to the propagation-invariant property of the Mathieu beams it should even be possible to stack multiple aligned particles along the optical axis. Figure 5.8 summarises the basic scheme with an even 4th order Mathieu beam.

The ellipticity parameter q of the Mathieu beams is an important degree of freedom when a potential landscape is optimised for elongated particles. Figure 5.9 shows an example where q is varied from very small to very large values. It can be seen that

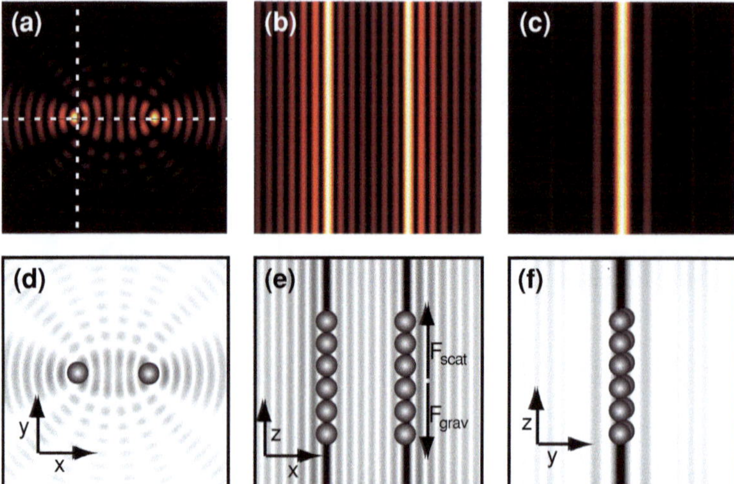

Fig. 5.7 Experimental scheme for optical moulding with Mathieu beams. An even 7th order Mathieu beam is used to create a three-dimensional structure of $2\,\mu$m silica spheres. The transverse (**a**) and axial (**b**), (**c**) field distributions give rise to an optical potential landscape, which is indicated in the linear approximation (cf. Eq. (2.5)) in (**d**)–(**f**). This optical potential confines spherical particles transversally in the two main intensity maxima. Along the optical axis, counteracting scattering and gravitational forces are in equilibrium

the symmetry of the transverse intensity distribution and thus the optical potential landscape undergoes a transition from circular to Cartesian symmetry. Numerical variations of q for different Mathieu beams show that for the developed experimental schemes, values of $q = 27$ should be well suited, assuming elongated particles with aspect ratios of roughly 1:2.

5.4.3 Experimental Validation

The developed experiments have been performed within the framework of the diploma thesis of Ms Christina Alpmann (Alpmann 2010) as a common research project at the University of Glasgow (Alpmann et al. 2010). The concrete setup differed from the generic setup described above in two points. First, the microscope where the optical trapping system was integrated was equipped with a stereoscopic viewing mode (Bowman et al. 2010) that allowed to verify the three-dimensional structure of the created microstructures. Furthermore, the refractive axicon and the positive lens depicted in Fig. 5.6 were emulated by a diffractive axicon on an SLM, which facilitated the optimisation of the axicon's angle and the lens' focal length interactively. The experimental parameters were numerical aperture of the microscope objective NA $= 1.3$, laser wavelength $\lambda = 671\,$nm, maximal laser output

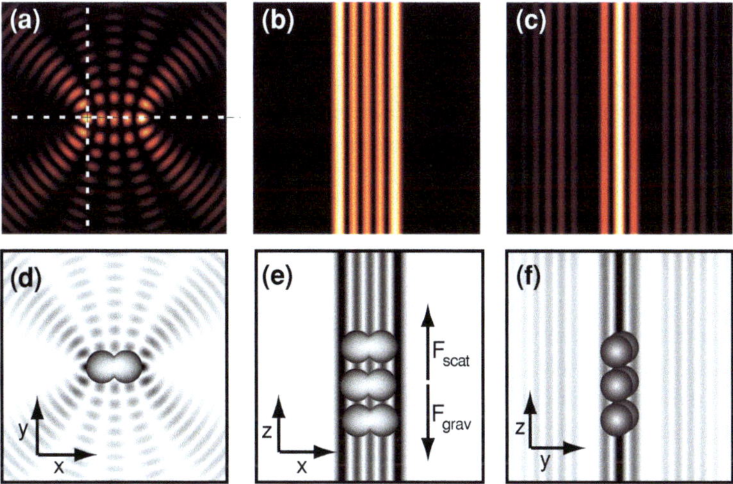

Fig. 5.8 Experimental scheme for optical moulding and alignment with Mathieu beams. An even 4th order Mathieu beam is used to align elongated particles of approximately $3 \times 5\,\mu$m and create a three-dimensional structure of multiple particles. The transverse (**a**) and axial (**b**), (**c**) field distributions give rise to an optical potential landscape, which is indicated in the linear approximation in (**d**)–(**f**). The transversally elliptical optical potential can align elongated particles with the long axis of the ellipsis. Along the optical axis, counteracting scattering and gravitational forces are in equilibrium

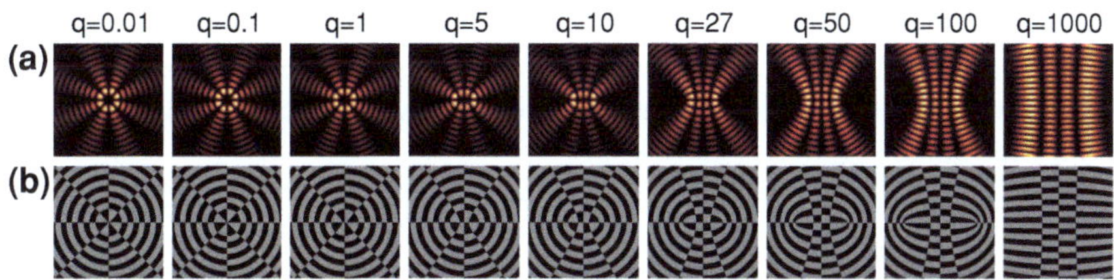

Fig. 5.9 Influence of the ellipticity q on the example of a M_4^o beam. **a** Transverse intensity distribution of the IG beam, calculated as $|M_4^o(\eta, \xi, q)|^2$ from Eq. (5.12); intensity is normalised and depicted in false colour for best visibility. **b** Corresponding phase distribution $\mathfrak{Im}\left(\log M_4^o(\eta, \xi, q)\right)$; the *bright* and *dark grey* values correspond to a phase of 0 and π, respectively

power $P_{max} = 300\,$mW, an emulated axicon apex angle $\alpha = 178.88°$ for an equivalent glass axicon (assuming $n_{glass} = 1.50$), and a positive diffractive lens behind the axicon with $f = 732.8\,$mm.

It was demonstrated that Mathieu beams indeed can be generated by the proposed method with pre-shaped ring illumination in the Fourier plane. With the experimental parameters chosen, the propagation-invariant distance was at least $2z_{max} \approx 11\,\mu$m compared to a Rayleigh length of a comparable Gaussian beam of less than $1\,\mu$m (Alpmann et al. 2010). Both proposed experiments have been performed successfully with this configuration. It was shown that at least two times six spherical $2\,\mu$m silica particles can be stacked in the two main maxima of the even 7th order Mathieu beam.

Furthermore, elongated silica particles of approximately 3×5 μm were successfully aligned in the optical potential well of an even 4th order Mathieu beam. It was achieved to stack two of these particles and even to rotate the whole structure with respect to the optical axis. Further details on the experimental results can be found in the corresponding publication (Alpmann et al. 2010).

5.5 Conclusion and Perspectives

The proposed and demonstrated concepts of optical micromanipulation with non-diffracting Mathieu beams offer new opportunities for various fields. In contrast to other, previously used non-diffracting beams like Bessel beams or the basic subset of helical Mathieu beams, the complete class of Mathieu beams offers an unrivalled diversity in transverse optical potential landscapes. Despite this complexity of the transverse beam profile, the Mathieu beams still offer all desired features of a non-diffracting beam, in particular its propagation-invariance and self-healing properties. Promising applications can be found, for example, in the organisation of matter, where the high degree of order of the transverse intensity profile of Mathieu beams can be directly transferred to a corresponding order of microscopic or nanoscopic particles. For the alignment and orientation of elongated particles, the light field can be tailored to the dimension and aspect ratio of the particles. On the one hand, the order of the Mathieu beam can be selected for maximal overlap of the intensity distribution with the particle. On the other hand, the eccentricity can be tuned to the aspect ratio of the particle, yielding a perfectly matching optical potential landscape for a wide range of different particles.

References

Alpmann C (2010) Maßgeschneiderte Lichtfelder zur mehrdimensionalen Manipulation von Materie in optischen Pinzetten. Master's thesis, Westfälische Wilhelms-Universität Münster

Alpmann C, Bowman R, Woerdemann M, Padgett M, Denz C (2010) Mathieu beams as versatile light moulds for 3D micro particle assemblies. Opt Express 18:26084–26091

Arlt J, Garces-Chavez V, Sibbett W, Dholakia K (2001) Optical micromanipulation using a Bessel light beam. Opt Commun 197:239–245

Arscott F (1964) Periodic differential equations. Pergamon Press, Oxford

Baumgartl J, Mazilu M, Dholakia K (2008) Optically mediated particle clearing using Airy wavepackets. Nat Photonics 2:675–678

Bélanger P, Rioux M (1978) Ring pattern of a lens-axicon doublet illuminated by a Gaussian beam. Appl Opt 17:1080–1088

Boguslawski M, Rose P, Denz C (2011) Nondiffracting kagome lattice. Appl Phys Lett 98:061111

Bowman R, Gibson G, Padgett M (2010) Particle tracking stereomicroscopy in optical tweezers: control of trap shape. Opt Express 18:11785–11790

Chavez-Cerda S, Gutierrez-Vega J, New G (2001) Elliptic vortices of electromagnetic wave fields. Opt Lett 26:1803–1805

Chavez-Cerda S, Padgett M, Allison I, New G, Gutierrez-Vega J, O'Neil A, MacVicar I, Courtial J (2002) Holographic generation and orbital angular momentum of high-order Mathieu beams. J Opt B: Quantum Semiclass Opt 4:S52–S57

Davis J, Guertin J, Cottrell D (1993) Diffraction-free beams generated with programmable spatial light modulators. Appl Opt 32:6368–6370

Davis J, Cottrell D, Campos J, Yzuel M, Moreno I (1999) Encoding amplitude information onto phase-only filters. Appl Opt 38:5004–5013

Durnin J (1987) Exact solutions for nondiffracting beams. I. The scalar theory. J Opt Soc Am A 4:651–654

Durnin J, Miceli J Jr., Eberly J (1987) Diffraction-free beams. Phys Rev Lett 58:1499–1501

Garcès-Chàvez V, McGloin D, Melville H, Sibbett W, Dholakia K (2002) Simultaneous micromanipulation in multiple planes using a self-reconstructing light beam. Nature 419:145–147

Garces-Chavez V, Volke-Sepulveda K, Chavez-Cerda S, Sibbett W, Dholakia K (2002) Transfer of orbital angular momentum to an optically trapped low-index particle. Phys Rev A 66:063402

Garces-Chavez V, McGloin D, Padgett M, Dultz W, Schmitzer H, Dholakia K (2003) Observation of the transfer of the local angular momentum density of a multiringed light beam to an optically trapped particle. Phys Rev Lett 91:093602

Gori F, Guattari G, Padovani C (1987) Bessel-Gauss beams. Opt Commun 64:491–495

Gutierrez-Vega J, Bandres M (2005) Helmholtz-Gauss waves. J Opt Soc Am A 22:289–298

Gutierrez-Vega J, Iturbe-Castillo M, Chavez-Cerda S (2000) Alternative formulation for invariant optical fields: Mathieu beams. Opt Lett 25:1493–1495

He H, Friese M, Heckenberg N, Rubinsztein-Dunlop H (1995) Direct observation of transfer of angular momentum to absorptive particles from a laser beam with a phase singularity. Phys Rev Lett 75:826–829

Lautanen J, Kettunen V, Laakkonen P, Turunen J (2000) High-efficiency production of propagation-invariant spot arrays . J Opt Soc Am A 17:2208–2215

Lopez-Mariscal C, Gutierrez-Vega J, Milne G, Dholakia K (2006) Orbital angular momentum transfer in helical Mathieu beams. Opt Express 14:4182–4187

Mazilu M, Stevenson D, Gunn-Moore F, Dholakia K (2009) Light beats the spread: non-diffracting beams. Laser Photon Rev 4:529–547

McGloin D, Dholakia K (2005) Bessel beams: diffraction in a new light. Contemp Phys 46:15–28

McLeod J (1954) The axicon: a new type of optical element. J Opt Soc Am 44:592

O'Neil AT, MacVicar I, Allen L, Padgett MJ (2002) Intrinsic and extrinsic nature of the orbital angular momentum of a light beam. Phys Rev Lett 88:053601

Scott G, McArdle N (1992) Efficient generation of nearly diffraction-free beams using an axicon. Opt Eng 31:2640–2643

Tatarkova S, Sibbett W, Dholakia K (2003) Brownian particle in an optical potential of the washboard type. Phys Rev Lett 91:038101

Turunen J, Friberg A (2010) Chapter: Propagation-invariant optical fields. In: Progress in optics, vol 54, Elsevier B. V, Amsterdam, pp 1–88

Turunen J, Vasara A, Friberg A (1988) Holographic generation of diffraction-free beams . Appl Opt 27:3959–3962

Turunen J, Vasara A, Friberg A (1991) Propagation invariance and self-imaging in variable-coherence optics. J Opt Soc Am A 8:282–289

Vasara A, Turunen J, Friberg A (1989) Realization of general nondiffracting beams with computer-generated holograms. J Opt Soc Am A 6:1748–1754

Volke-Sepulveda K, Garces-Chavez V, Chavez-Cerda S, Arlt J, Dholakia K (2002) Orbital angular momentum of a high-order Bessel light beam. J Opt B: Quantum Semiclass Opt 4:82–89

Volke-Sepulveda K, Chavez-Cerda S, Garces-Chavez V, Dholakia K (2004) Three-dimensional optical forces and transfer of orbital angular momentum from multiringed light beams to spherical microparticles. J Opt Soc Am B 21:1749–1757

Zwick S, Haist T, Warber M, Osten W (2010) Dynamic holography using pixelated light modulators. Appl Opt 49:F47–F58

Chapter 6
Ince-Gaussian Beams for the Optical Organisation of Microparticles

Self-similar beams are by far the most prominent class of laser beams as they are natural solutions to the resonator problem and hence widely available as output of commercial and research lasers. In contrast to, for example, non-diffracting beams, self-similar beams maintain their transverse shape during propagation but scale during free-space propagation or when passing optical elements. This enables strong axial intensity gradients of focused beams that are important for three-dimensional optical trapping and furthermore ensures that the optical potential landscape is equal in any transverse plane, except for the (known) scaling factor. Moreover, helical Laguerre-Gaussian beams are known to carry optical orbital angular momentum. Despite their diversity, however, the vast majority of applications demonstrated so far in optical trapping is restricted to the fundamental Gaussian beam and other lower order Hermite-Gaussian or Laguerre-Gaussian beams. The recently found fundamental class of Ince-Gaussian modes is the general solution of the paraxial Helmholtz equation in elliptical coordinates and thus includes Hermite-Gaussian and Laguerre-Gaussian beams, which are the respective solutions in Cartesian and circular coordinates. With eccentricity as a parameter, Ince-Gaussian beams offer significantly higher diversity of transverse beam profiles and thus optical trapping potential landscapes. In this chapter, the potential of Ince-Gaussian beams for optical trapping applications is evaluated and the first experimental proof of optical micro-manipulation with Ince-Gaussian beams is demonstrated.

6.1 Self-Similar Solutions of the Paraxial Helmholtz Equation

The complex amplitude of the lowest order Gaussian beam is given by the well known equation (Saleh and Teich 2008)

$$\Psi_G(\vec{r}) = \frac{\omega_0}{\omega(z)} \exp\left(\frac{-r^2}{\omega^2(z)} - \mathrm{i}\frac{kr^2}{2R(z)} + \mathrm{i}\arctan(z/z_R) \right), \tag{6.1}$$

M. Woerdemann, *Structured Light Fields*, Springer Theses,
DOI: 10.1007/978-3-642-29323-8_6, © Springer-Verlag Berlin Heidelberg 2012

with the radial coordinate r, the beam width $\omega^2(z) = \omega_0^2(1 + z^2/z_R^2)$, the beam waist $\omega_0 = \omega(z = 0)$, the Rayleigh range $z_R = k\omega_0^2/2$, the phase front curvature $R(z) = z + z_R^2/z$, and the Gouy phase shift $\arctan(z/z_R) \equiv \Phi_G(z)$. This fundamental Gaussian beam is widespread in (laser) optics and has exciting properties. For example, the Gaussian beam will maintain its transverse beam profile, apart from a scaling factor, during propagation or when it is affected by a lens; i.e. it is a *self-similar* beam.

Gaussian beams are eigenmodes of typical laser resonators and often desired as output due to their comperatively simple—i.e. homogeneous—beam profile and, for example, are used as experimental plane-wave approximations within their Rayleigh range. Besides an uncountable number of further beneficial properties, Gaussian beams can be focused to a diffraction limited spot, which is essential for applications in optical tweezers (cf. Chap. 2). For many advanced applications, however, higher order modes are required that exhibit more complex features of the wavefront. The well known Hermite-Gaussian (HG) and Laguerre-Gaussian (LG) beams each represent a whole class of self-similar beams that feature more complex transverse field distributions, including highly structured intensity patterns and inclined phase fronts that can carry orbital angular momentum. Recently, a new class of self-similar beams, the *Ince-Gaussian* (IG) beams, has been proposed (Bandres and Gutierrez-Vega 2004). These IG beams are solutions to the paraxial wave equation in elliptic cylindrical coordinates and thus include HG and LG beams in the limiting case of a circular or rectangular (i.e. Cartesian) cylindrical coordinates. The most general class of IG beams, hence, includes all desirable properties of HG and LG beams and adds a new dimension, the ellipticity. This should result in a significantly larger range of possible optical potential landscapes and give rise to exciting novel applications in optical micromanipulation.

For a more systematic mathematical description, we consider the paraxial Helmholtz equation.

$$\left(\nabla_t^2 - 2ik\frac{\partial}{\partial z}\right)\Psi(\vec{r}) = 0. \tag{6.2}$$

This equation is solved by the complex, slowly varying amplitude $\Psi(\vec{r})$ and gives the paraxial beam $P(\vec{r})$ that propagates in $+z$ direction:

$$P(\vec{r}) = \Psi(\vec{r})\exp(ikz). \tag{6.3}$$

Well known exact solutions for $\Psi(\vec{r})$ are the HG and LG beams, which are two complete families of orthogonal solutions. In order to get corresponding solutions in elliptic coordinates, the following ansatz is considered (Bandres and Gutierrez-Vega 2004):

$$\Psi_{\mathrm{IG}}(\vec{r}) = E(\xi)N(\eta)\exp(iZ(z))\Psi_G(\vec{r}), \tag{6.4}$$

with the real functions E, N, Z in the elliptical coordinates given by Eqs. (5.8) and (5.9). Inserting this ansatz into the paraxial wave equation and using the fact that $\Psi_G(\vec{r})$ already satisfies that equation, the following set of ordinary differential equations is obtained (Bandres and Gutierrez-Vega 2004):

$$\frac{d^2 E}{d\xi^2} - \epsilon \sinh 2\xi \frac{dE}{d\xi} - (a - p\epsilon \cosh 2\xi)E = 0 \qquad (6.5)$$

$$\frac{d^2 N}{d\eta^2} + \epsilon \sin 2\eta \frac{dN}{d\eta} + (a - p\epsilon \cos 2\eta)N = 0 \qquad (6.6)$$

$$-\left(\frac{z^2 + z_R^2}{z_R}\right) \frac{dZ}{dz} = p. \qquad (6.7)$$

Here, p, a are separation constants, $\epsilon = 2f_0^2/\omega_0^2$ is the ellipticity parameter, and Z can be easily identified as $Z(z) = -p \arctan(z/z_R)$. Equation (6.6) is known as the *Ince equation* (Ince 1923; Arscott 1964), while Eq. (6.5) can be derived from Eq. (6.6) with the substitution $\eta = \mathrm{i}\xi$. The Ince equation is solved by $C_p^m(\eta, \epsilon)$ and $S_p^m(\eta, \epsilon)$, the even and odd Ince polynomials of order p and degree m. Order and degree always have the same parity and they are related according $0 \leq m \leq p$ for the even functions and $1 \leq m \leq p$ for the odd functions. Details of the Ince polynomials and their computation are provided in Appendix B.2. With these solutions, the even ($\mathrm{IG}_{p,m}^{\mathrm{e}}$) and odd ($\mathrm{IG}_{p,m}^{\mathrm{o}}$) IG beams according to Eq. (6.4) can be written as:

$$\mathrm{IG}_{p,m}^{\mathrm{e}}(\vec{r}, \epsilon) = \frac{A\omega_0}{w(z)} C_p^m(\mathrm{i}\xi, \epsilon)C_p^m(\eta, \epsilon)$$

$$\times \exp\left[\left(\frac{-r^2}{\omega^2(z)}\right) + \mathrm{i}\left(kz + \frac{kr^2}{2R(z)} - (p+1)\Phi_G(z)\right)\right] \qquad (6.8)$$

$$\mathrm{IG}_{p,m}^{\mathrm{o}}(\vec{r}, \epsilon) = \frac{B\omega_0}{w(z)} S_p^m(\mathrm{i}\xi, \epsilon)S_p^m(\eta, \epsilon)$$

$$\times \exp\left[\left(\frac{-r^2}{\omega^2(z)}\right) + \mathrm{i}\left(kz + \frac{kr^2}{2R(z)} - (p+1)\Phi_G(z)\right)\right], \qquad (6.9)$$

with the normalising constants A, B. Besides even and odd IG beams, it is possible to construct helical IG beams (HIG) as a superposition of even and odd IG beams (Bentley et al. 2006):

$$\mathrm{HIG}_{p,m}^{\pm}(\vec{r}, \epsilon) = \mathrm{IG}_{p,m}^{\mathrm{e}}(\vec{r}, \epsilon) \pm \mathrm{i}\,\mathrm{IG}_{p,m}^{\mathrm{o}}(\vec{r}, \epsilon) \qquad 1 \leq m \leq p \qquad (6.10)$$

These beams feature optical vortices (Allen et al. 1992), i.e. an azimuthal inclination of the wavefront, and thus carry optical orbital angular momentum similar to a subset of the LG beams and helical Mathieu beams.

IG beams form a third complete orthogonal set of solutions of the paraxial wave equation, i.e. any paraxial wave can be written as a sum of IG beams. IG beams are defined in elliptic cylindrical coordinates in contrast to HG beams in Cartesian coordinates and LG beams in circular cylindrical coordinates. If the ellipticity is

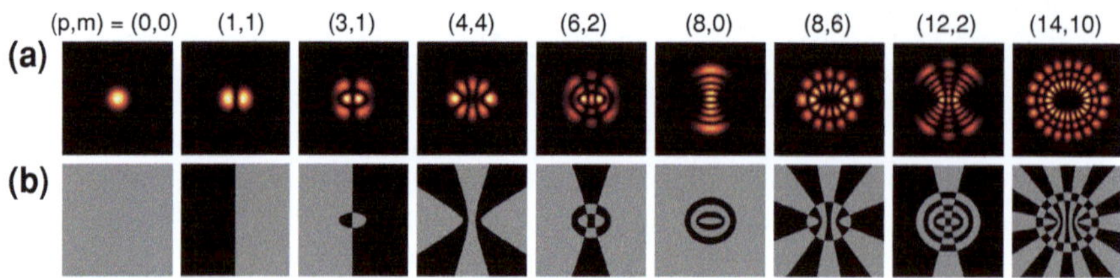

Fig. 6.1 Selection of even IG beams of order p and degree m ($\text{IG}^{e}_{p,m}$). **a** Transverse intensity distribution of the IG beam, calculated as $|\text{IG}^{e}_{p,m}(\vec{r}, \epsilon)|^2$ from Eq. (6.8); intensity is normalised and depicted in false colour for better visibility. **b** Corresponding phase distribution $\Im\big(\log \text{IG}^{e}_{p,m}(\vec{r}, \epsilon)\big)$; the *bright* and *dark grey* values correspond to a phase of 0 and π, respectively. The field distributions are identical in any transverse plane, except for a radial scaling factor

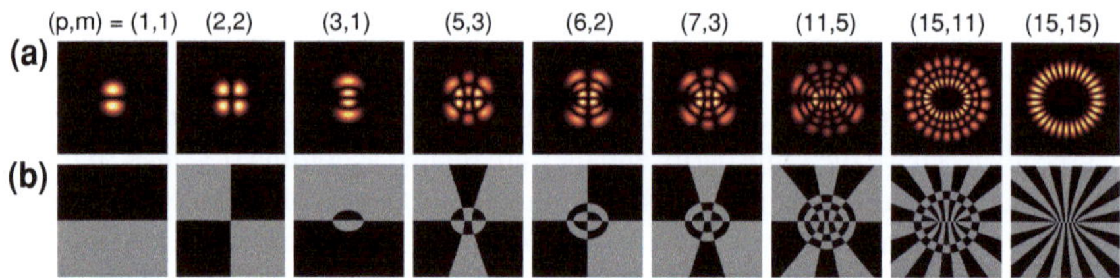

Fig. 6.2 Selection of odd IG beams of order p and degree m ($\text{IG}^{o}_{p,m}$). **a** Transverse intensity distribution of the IG beam, calculated as $|\text{IG}^{o}_{p,m}(\vec{r}, \epsilon)|^2$ from Eq. (6.9); intensity is normalised and depicted in false colour for better visibility. **b** Corresponding phase distribution $\Im\big(\log \text{IG}^{o}_{p,m}(\vec{r}, \epsilon)\big)$; the *bright* and *dark grey* values correspond to a phase of 0 and π, respectively. The field distributions are identical in any transverse plane, except for a radial scaling factor

chosen as $\epsilon = 0$, they represent LG beams and for $\epsilon = \infty$ they represent HG beams. By inspecting Eqs. (6.8) and (6.9), we find a number of interesting properties. The lowest order IG beam IG^{0}_{0} is identical to the fundamental Gaussian beam because $C^{0}_{0}(i\xi, \epsilon) \equiv 1$. For all higher orders, the transverse beam profile is defined by the product of the two Ince polynomials. Furthermore, propagation is governed by the usual Rayleigh range and Gouy phase shift $\Phi_{G}(z)$ with an additional phase term $p\Phi_{G}(z)$ that depends on the order p. A selection of transverse field distributions of even, odd, and helical IG beams is provided in Figs. 6.1, 6.2, and 6.3, respectively, showing their transverse intensity and phase distributions.

6.2 Ince-Gaussian Beams as Optical Traps

The fundamental Gaussian beam and the $\text{LG}^{\ell}_{p=0}$ beams that carry an orbital angular momentum of $\hbar\ell$ are the most prominent laser modes used in optical trapping

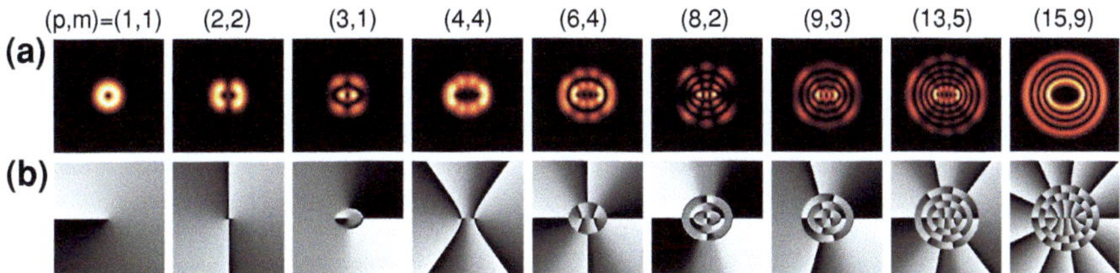

Fig. 6.3 Selection of helical IG beams of order p and degree m ($\mathrm{HIG}^{\pm}_{p,m}$). **a** Transverse intensity distribution of the IG beam, calculated as $|\mathrm{HIG}^{\pm}_{p,m}(\vec{r},\epsilon)|^2$ from Eq. (6.10); intensity is normalised and depicted in false colour for better visibility. **b** Corresponding phase distribution $\Im\!\left(\log \mathrm{HIG}^{\pm}_{p,m}(\vec{r},\epsilon)\right)$; the *grey* values correspond to a phase interval of 0 to 2π. The field distributions are identical in any transverse plane, except for a radial scaling factor

applications. Various approaches have been proposed to convert the fundamental beam into higher order LG beams (Heckenberg et al. 1992; Kennedy et al. 2002; Machavariani et al. 2002). Higher order HG beams have been used, for example, to align non-spherical particles (Sato et al. 1991). For advanced state-of-the-art applications, however, HG and LG often are not versatile enough because the range of possible transverse field distributions is limited. One powerful approach for the two-dimensional structuring of a trapping light field are holographic optical tweezers (HOT, cf. Chap. 7). HOT can provide almost arbitrary configurations in discrete layers that are calculated either iteratively or as a superposition of diffractive lenses and gratings. With three-dimensional generalisations of the iterative algorithms, also arbitrary three-dimensional intensity distributions can be approximated within the physically realisable limits (Whyte and Courtial 2005)—but the task remains computationally expensive. More importantly, however, the propagation properties of the resulting light fields are undefined in a sense that the intensity distribution is only defined in a volume considered by the algorithm, and the optical phase serves as the free parameter.

IG beams can bridge the gap between the relatively simple HG and LG beams with their desired propagation properties and the discrete structuring of a light field as it is used in HOT. First, we consider typical features of the transverse field distribution of IG beams, which changes significantly with the choice of even, odd, or helical solutions, the order p and degree m, and finally the chosen ellipticity ϵ. Analogous to the families of HG and LG beams, the lowest order IG beam—i.e. $\mathrm{IG}^{e}_{0,0}$ —is the fundamental Gaussian beam (cf. Fig. 6.1). For the special choice $\epsilon \to 0$, i.e. for circular symmetric coordinates, the IG beams approach corresponding LG beams. In this limit, any LG^{ℓ}_{p} beam is represented by a specific IG beam with a simple conversion of the IG parameters p, m into corresponding parameters of the LG beam (Bandres and Gutierrez-Vega 2004). Similarly, any HG_{n_x,n_y} beam is represented by a corresponding IG beam if $\epsilon \to \infty$ and a simple conversion of the parameters n_x, n_y is performed. Hence, the IG beams constitute the exact and continuous transition between LG and HG beams, and include both families (Bandres and Gutierrez-Vega 2004). An example of the influence of the ellipticity on the beam

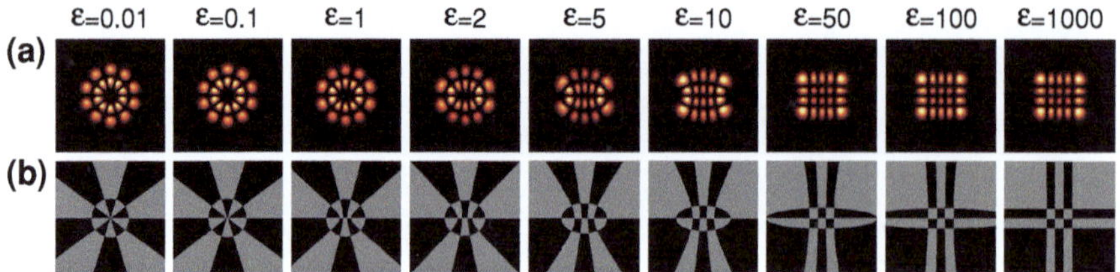

Fig. 6.4 Influence of the ellipticity ϵ on the example of a $IG^o_{5,3}$ beam. **a** Transverse intensity distribution of the IG beam, calculated as $|IG^o_{5,3}(\vec{r}, \epsilon)|^2$ from Eq. (6.9); intensity is normalised and depicted in false colour for better visibility. **b** Corresponding phase distribution $\Im m\big(\log IG^o_{5,3}(\vec{r}, \epsilon)\big)$; the *bright* and *dark grey* values correspond to a phase of 0 and π, respectively

shape is given in Fig. 6.4. The transition regime with finite, non-zero ϵ certainly is the most important advantage of IG beams for optical trapping applications. As depicted in Figs. 6.1a, 6.2a, and 6.3a, the transverse intensity distribution can be rather complex but always shows a high degree of order. For a given ellipticity and a fixed order p, there are $p + 1$ different even IG beams, p odd IG beams, and p helical IG beams defined. The envelope changes from a more vertical[1] distribution for small values of m to elliptical shapes for $m \approx p$. In radial direction, intensity maxima are separated by $(p - m)/2$ nodal lines of zero intensity. These lines, also known as *edge dislocations* of the wavefront (Basistiy et al. 1995), are accompanied by a corresponding phase shift of π. Furthermore, the even and odd IG beams feature hyperbolic nodal lines whose number is given by the degree m for even IG beams and by $(m - 1)$ for odd IG beams, respectively, also accompanied by a phase shift of π. Odd IG beams additionally possess one nodal line on the horizontal axis of symmetry, $\xi = 0$. Helical IG beams do not have obvious hyperbolic nodal lines but rather possess a phase distribution that is a continuous function of the angular coordinate η and associated with m phase vortices, or *screw dislocations*, of the wavefront (Basistiy et al. 1995). The manifold range of complex intensity distributions can be expected to lead to an equal diversity of transverse optical potential landscapes that adopt the order and structure of the respective distributions. Furthermore, the emergence of optical vortices could lead to a transfer of not only linear but also angular optical momentum to optically trapped matter.

Higher order IG beams have larger widths than lower order beams (Bandres and Gutierrez-Vega 2004). During propagation, IG beams scale like $\omega_0/\omega(z)$, owing to their relationship with the fundamental Gaussian beam, but remain self-similar. For optical trapping applications, this behaviour has a number of implications. To begin with, IG beams for optical trapping can be generated in any plane, including any conjugate plane of the trapping plane, any Fourier plane or any other plane in the

---

[1]   The use of "vertical" and "horizontal" is connected with the definition of the elliptical coordinates in Sect. 6.1. For experimental applications the system of coordinates can, of course, be rotated by any arbitrary angle.

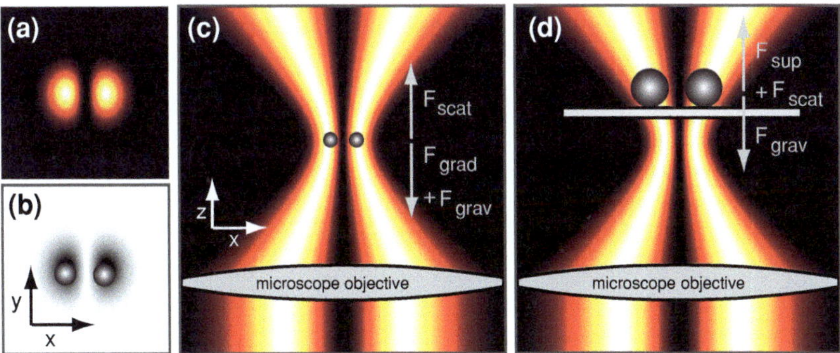

Fig. 6.5 Configuration for optical micromanipulation with IG beams. Transverse intensity distribution of an $IG^e_{1,1}$ beam (**a**) and corresponding lateral potential landscape in linear approximation (**b**). In propagation direction, the focused beam enables two modes of operation: Three dimensional trapping in the focal plane (**c**) and optical guiding and organisation in a working plane further away from the focal plane (**d**). Indicated forces are scattering force (F_{scat}), gradient force (F_{grad}), gravitational force (F_{grav}), and support force (F_{supp})

optical path. This means, IG beams are perfectly compatible with holographic optical tweezers, where holographic beam shaping usually takes place in the Fourier plane but, on the other hand, possible experiments are by no means limited to this configuration. Besides the generation of IG beams, their behaviour in the vicinity of the focal plane is vital for their performance in optical micromanipulation. The particular propagation behaviour of focused IG beams leads to two modes of operation.[2] First, it is possible to utilise the axial intensity gradients in order to achieve an equilibrium between gradient forces, scattering forces, and gravitational forces. This operation mode (cf. Fig. 6.5c) is typically used in (holographic) optical tweezers. With the introduction of IG beams the functionality of optical tweezers could be significantly extended, owing to the complex optical landscapes available. However, typical sizes of the transverse substructure of IG beams are below a few hundred nanometres in the close vicinity of the focal plane. Hence, this mode of operation is optimal for smaller particles, including nanoparticles. Although initial experiments with the first operation mode have been successful and promising, in the following the focus will be on the second mode of operation, the optical organisation of microparticles. In this mode, not a three-dimensional confinement of single particles close to the focal plane is envisaged but an extended optical potential landscape is created that biases suspended particles to assemble themselves in structures imprinted by the light field.

---

[2] In the following, we assume that the qualitative behaviour of strongly focused IG beams is reasonably described within the paraxial regime. A brief discussion on the validity of this approximation in optical trapping scenarios is provided in Sect. 2.4.

6.3 Organising Microparticles with IG Beams

One of the major advantages of IG beams, besides their transverse profile, is their propagation behaviour and in particular their self-similarity. In consequence, one can easily determine the transverse optical potential well and, more importantly, the transition from one transverse plane to another is highly continuous, without abrupt changes in the quality of the potential landscape. This behaviour can be well utilised in a configuration as depicted in Fig. 6.5d. The crucial idea is that it is not only the focal plane that can be used directly for optical micromanipulation but rather a plane where the focused beam has spread already. By means of an optically transparent support, e.g. a microscope cover slip, a working plane in the vicinity of the focal plane is selected. The working plane can be chosen so that the IG beam already has spread slightly and thus the dimension of its substructure can be matched perfectly with the dimensions of the particles to be influenced. Depending on the distance between the actual working plane and the focal plane, the forces acting on the particle are related differently. The gravitational force F_{grav}, of course, is constant for all cases. For distances which are large compared with the Rayleigh length of the focused beam, the gradient force F_{grad} along the optical axis is negligible because the axial intensity gradient decreases rapidly with an increasing distance from the focal plane. In a similar way, the radiation force F_{scat} along the optical axis is decreased and the transverse potential well is flattened. The situation depicted in Fig. 6.5d assumes that the gravitational force is dominant and compensated by the counteracting force of the support, leading to an axial equilibrium position. In this situation the transverse gradient forces can play a significant role as long as they are in the order of or larger than the thermal forces acting on the particles and the interaction with the surface can be neglected.[3] Already a shallow potential well, or optical potential landscape, can bias the natural Brownian motion under these conditions, leading to the concept of optically guided self-assembly, i.e. favour the random walk of particles until they organise themselves in structures imprinted by the optical potential. Moreover, sedimenting particles can already be influenced when they are still far above the actual working plane. In this case, with a proper choice of experimental parameters, the particles might be guided during sedimentation along lines of maximal intensity or minimal potential energy until they reach their final destination on the support. By this means, particles could be gathered up efficiently from a large volume within the suspension and the converging light field acts as an optical funnel, concentrating particles at the working plane.

For the experimental demonstration of the optical organisation of microparticles, the setup depicted in Fig. 6.6a has been developed and implemented. It is based on a generic holographic optical tweezers setup as discussed in Sect. 7.1.3. The basis is

---

[3] Typical microparticles like silica spheres and also silicate glass surfaces exhibit negative surface charges in aqueous solutions (Behrens and Grier 2001). If the solvent has very low ionic strength, like pure water, the repelling forces due to the electric double layers (Israelachvili 2011) usually maintain a separation between particles and surface and thus suppress other short-range interactions and the particles are free to move along the surface.

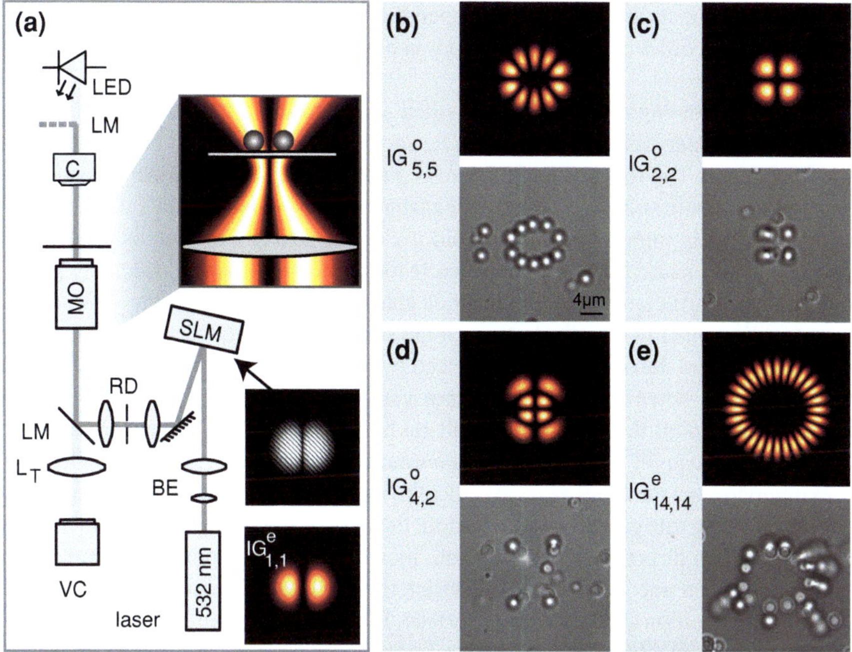

Fig. 6.6 Experimental setup for optical organisation with IG beams (**a**). *BE* beam expansion; *RD* relay optics and diaphragm, selecting the first order of diffraction; *LM* laser line mirror; L_T, tube lens; *MO* microscope objective; *C* condenser; *VC* video camera. Optically assembled micro structures (**b**)–(**e**) (*bottom*) and corresponding IG intensity pattern (**b**)–(**e**) (*top*). **b** 10 silica spheres, organised on an $IG^o_{5,5}$ beam. (**c**)–(**e**) Organisation and optical binding in an $IG^o_{2,2}$ beam, $IG^o_{4,2}$ beam, and $IG^e_{14,14}$ beam, respectively

an inverted optical microscope with a high numerical aperture microscope objective ($M = 100\,\text{x}$, $NA = 1.3$). A laser beam ($P_{max} = 2.5\,\text{W}$, $\lambda = 532\,\text{nm}$) is expanded and collimated so that it entirely illuminates the active area of a phase-only SLM. The SLM is an "X8267-16" model from Hamamatsu Photonics with 768×768 active pixels that can introduce a phase-shift of at least 2π. The SLM plane is imaged onto the back aperture of the microscope objective, ensuring a Fourier relation between the focal plane of the objective and the SLM plane. A blue ($\lambda \approx 470\,\text{nm}$) LED and a condenser lens provide the microscope illumination. The illumination and image beam path of the microscope is separated from the laser beam path by means of two laser line mirrors that selectively reflect at $\lambda = 532\,\text{nm}$ and transmit the remaining visible spectrum.

Tailored holograms for the generation of IG beams are calculated from the complex electric field distribution, defined by Eqs. (6.8) and (6.9), with an ellipticity $\epsilon = 2$. The phase and amplitude information of the respective IG beam is encoded in one phase-only hologram by means of a carrier frequency that enables amplitude modulation. Details of the modulation of the complex wavefront with phase-only diffractive elements are provided in Appendix A. The IG beams are generated in the first diffraction order and the zeroth order is blocked in an intermediate plane before the microscope.

For the following demonstrations, silica spheres with a diameter $d = 1.5\,\mu m$, dispersed in water were used. Figure 6.5d shows the configuration in the vicinity of the focal plane. The focus of an IG beam is placed slightly beneath the bottom of the sample chamber in such a way that the beam has already widened a little when it enters the fluid. This is important first to avoid undesired strong axial intensity gradients and second to ensure that the transversal features of the IG beams' intensity pattern are separated sufficiently. When the silica spheres are dispersed in the sample, they start to sediment slowly to the bottom of the sample chamber. During sedimentation they begin to feel the optical forces induced by the intensity gradients of the IG beam structure, even when the spheres are not yet close to the surface. At this point it becomes important that the shape of all IG beams is invariant during propagation. If a particle is caught in an intensity maximum at any height, it is guided along the maximum toward the focus as in an optical funnel and finally finds its position on the support. During this guided sedimentation, the optical scattering forces, which act in the propagation direction of the IG beam, increase. Thus, the power of the IG beam has to be chosen adequately low, otherwise the particles are elevated and find their equilibrium position above the glass surface. For the $d = 1.5\,\mu m$ silica spheres used in the experiments described, typically, laser power of a few milliwatts, measured before the microscope objective, was employed; the actual value was adapted to the transversal extent of the respective IG beam and the distance between surface and focal plane. Figure 6.6b shows an experimental result of organisation in an $IG_{5,5}^o$ beam. Ten silica spheres occupy positions according to the ten intensity maxima of the IG beam. With structures that can accommodate more than a few particles, usually not all possible positions are occupied purely by sedimentation, depending on the concentration of dispersed particles in the fluid. The fully occupied ring of ten particles was achieved by translating the pattern of already trapped particles relative to the surface, to positions where other particles are sedimented and can be used to complete the structure.

For the assembly in Fig. 6.6c, an $IG_{2,2}^o$ beam with four distinct intensity maxima was placed at a location where eight particles were sedimented close to each other. Directly after the beam is switched on, the particles organise themselves in the pattern that is imprinted by the particular IG beam. As there are more particles than intensity maxima, the surplus particles seem to pile up in the structure. This highly interesting feature of the experimental configuration can be better seen in Fig. 6.6d. An $IG_{4,2}^o$ beam is used and particles are confined in the outer four intensity maxima. The inner maxima show a slightly inhomogeneous intensity distribution and are not appropriately separated to trap individual particles of the used size at each position. The outer maxima, however, do not accommodate one but two particles each, piled up in columns or chains that follow the shape of the diverging IG beam. The complete, three-dimensional structure remains intact, even when the sample chamber and thus the surface is translated relative to the structure. Most likely these chains are induced by longitudinal optical binding (Mohanty et al. 2008). In a simplified model of optical binding, the first sphere focuses parts of the incident light and the next particle is trapped close to this focus (Dholakia and Zemanek 2010). Following this model one can estimate particle-particle separations of $d_{\mathrm{pp}} \approx 4.3\,\mu$m for plane incident wavefronts. Although the particle-particle separations cannot be measured accurately with the current setup, it can be estimated by defocusing and observation that it is close to zero and thus closer than predicted by the simple model. This can well be explained by the additional gravitational force that compresses the chains and reduces the interparticle distances. A good approach to the further investigation of the binding would be the integration of a stereoscopic viewing mode (Alpmann 2010).

The optically bound chains can be much longer than two particles as shown in Fig. 6.6e. The depicted structure is assembled by using an $\mathrm{IG}^{\mathrm{e}}_{14,14}$ beam. The feature size of the structure is too small for all possible positions being occupied by particles. Instead, remaining particles form chains of four to five particles, which can easily be proved by turning off the IG beam and counting the sedimenting particles. During a series of experiments, even longer chains with up to ten and more bound particles each have been observed. The structures are solely held together by optical forces; once the IG beam is turned off, the particles sediment and disperse immediately.[4]

6.4 Conclusion and Perspectives

The utilisation of the family of IG beams for the optically guided organisation of multiple microscale particles has been proposed and demonstrated. IG beams include important properties of the well known HG and LG beams as they are a more general solution of the paraxial wave equation but feature substantially higher diversity in transversal intensity patterns and thus versatility in the range of possible optical landscapes and accessible degree of organisation. The self-similarity of IG beams facilitates their generation in almost any arbitrary plane along the beam path, including the Fourier plane of the microscope objective's focal plane. It furthermore allows choosing the working plane freely in the vicinity of the focal plane, adapted to the dimensions of the envisaged colloidal structures. Besides two-dimensional organisation, complex three-dimensional microstructures can be achieved utilising optical binding. The demonstrated examples might have exciting applications for coupled optical microresonator (Soria et al. 2011; Schweiger et al. 2007) experiments of hitherto unknown complexity.

---

[4] The experiments discussed in this section were performed in collaboration with Ms Christina Alpmann within the framework of her diploma thesis (Alpmann 2010) and have resulted in a joint publication (Woerdemann et al. 2011).

References

Allen L, Beijersbergen M, Spreeuw R, Woerdman J (1992) Orbital angular momentum of light and the transformation of laguerre-gaussian laser modes. Phys Rev A 45:8185–8189

Alpmann C (2010) Maßgeschneiderte Lichtfelder zur mehrdimensionalen Manipulation von Materie in optischen Pinzetten. Master's thesis, Westfälische Wilhelms-Universität Münster

Arscott F (1964) Periodic differential equations. Pergamon Press, Oxford

Bandres M, Gutierrez-Vega J (2004) Ince Gaussian beams. Opt Lett 29:144–146

Bandres M, Gutierrez-Vega J (2004) Ince-Gaussian modes of the paraxial wave equation and stable resonators. J Opt Soc Am A 21:873–880

Basistiy I, Soskin M, Vasnetsov M (1995) Optical wave-front dislocations and their properties. Opt Commun 119:604–612

Behrens S, Grier D (2001) The charge of glass and silica surfaces. J Chem Phys 115:6716–6721

Bentley J, Davis J, Bandres M, Gutierrez-Vega J (2006) Generation of helical Ince-Gaussian beams with a liquid-crystal display. Opt Lett 31:649–651

Dholakia K, Zemanek P (2010) Colloquium: gripped by light: optical binding. Rev Mod Phys 82:1767

Heckenberg N, McDuff R, Smith C, White A (1992) Generation of optical phase singularities by computer-generated holograms. Opt Lett 17:221–223

Ince E (1923) A linear differential equation with periodic coefficients. Proc London Math Soc 23:56–74

Israelachvili J (2011) Intramolecular and surface forces. Academic, London

Kennedy S, Szabo M, Teslow H, Porterfield J, Abraham E (2002) Creation of Laguerre-Gaussian laser modes using diffractive optics. Phys Rev A 66:043801

Machavariani G, Davidson N, Hasman E, Blit S, Ishaaya A, Friesem A (2002) Efficient conversion of a Gaussian beam to a high purity helical beam. Opt Commun 209:265–271

Mohanty S, Mohanty K, Berns M (2008) Organization of microscale objects using a microfabricated optical fiber. Opt Lett 33:2155–2157

Saleh B, Teich M (2008) Grundlagen der Photonik. Wiley-VCH, Berlin

Sato S, Ishigure M, Inaba H (1991) Optical trapping and rotational manipulation of microscopic particles and biological cells using higher-order mode Nd-YAG laser-beams. Electron Lett 27:1831–1832

Schweiger G, Nett R, Weigel T (2007) Microresonator array for high-resolution spectroscopy. Opt Lett 32:2644–2646

Soria S, Berneschi S, Brenci M, Cosi F, Conti G, Pelli S, Righini G (2011) Optical microspherical resonators for biomedical sensing. Sensors 11:785–805

Whyte G, Courtial J (2005) Experimental demonstration of holographic three-dimensional light shaping using a Gerchberg Saxton algorithm. New J Phys 7:117–128

Woerdemann M, Alpmann C, Denz C (2011) Optical assembly of microparticles into highly ordered structures using Ince-Gaussian beams. Appl Phys Lett 98:111101

Chapter 7
Holographic Optical Tweezers

Holographic optical tweezers (HOT) employ a relatively simple form of holographic beam-shaping that produces discrete, point-like intensity peaks in the optical trapping plane, each of which acts as a single optical tweezer. For each tweezer, lateral position and axial position can be determined individually by means of accordingly prepared holograms that split the incident wave front and set propagation angles and divergence properties. After a short discussion on the fundamental concepts of HOT and a brief review of the extensive literature emphasising applications in colloidal sciences, this chapter introduces two novel applications of HOT. The first application addresses the urgent demand for full position and orientation control on rod-shaped bacteria. These bacteria are representatives of a large class of biological cells with highly complex biophysical properties. For detailed imaging and access to biomechanical or cooperative properties, a versatile positioning and alignment scheme is developed. The second application demonstrates the potential of HOT in the area of supramolecular organisation of nanocontainers. While the arrangement and organisation of loaded nanocontainers is a broad field in chemistry, most available methods only work on ensembles of a huge number of particles and lack any fine control on individual particles. HOT are shown to be a versatile tool for selection, arrangement and organisation of single and multiple individual container particles.

7.1 Basic Concepts of Holographic Optical Tweezers

While the simplest implementation of optical tweezers relies on a stationary laser beam focused through a high numerical aperture lens, dynamic control increases the versatility significantly. From the discussion in Sect. 2.6 it is clear that position control of single optical tweezers can be achieved by controlling angle and divergence of the constituting laser beam by means of *diffractive optical elements* (DOEs). Furthermore, by appropriate multiplexing schemes, a multitude of independent optical tweezers can be realised. In state-of-the-art HOT applications, the DOE is usually

M. Woerdemann, *Structured Light Fields*, Springer Theses,
DOI: 10.1007/978-3-642-29323-8_7, © Springer-Verlag Berlin Heidelberg 2012

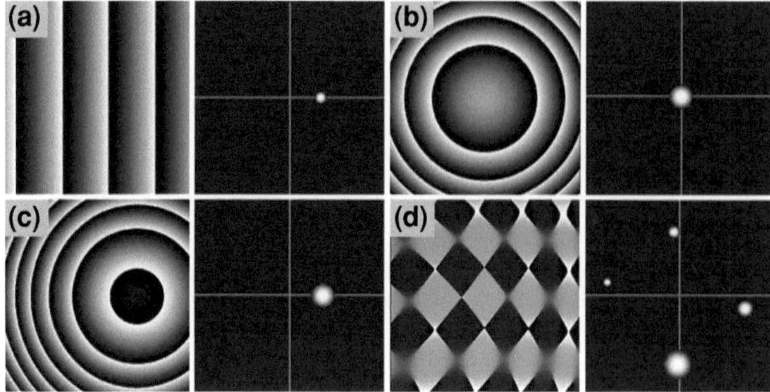

Fig. 7.1 Basic function of DOEs in HOT. Each subfigure shows the phase distribution of a DOE in grey values (*left*) and the resulting position of the optical trap in the specimen plane (*right*). The position of the trap along the beam axis is indicated by the diameter of the point marking the position in the specimen plane. From (Woerdemann et al. 2012)

realised by computer-addressable spatial light modulator (SLM) rather than a static diffractive element.

7.1.1 Diffractive Optical Elements

A general grating is known to diffract an illuminating light wave into several diffraction orders. The blazed diffraction grating depicted in Fig. 7.1a in contrast deflects light into only one diffraction order with an angle Θ. With the grating periods Λ_x, Λ_y the phase distribution of the grating is given by:

$$\phi(x, y) = \left(\frac{2\pi}{\Lambda_x}x + \frac{2\pi}{\Lambda_y}y \right) \quad \mathrm{mod}\ 2\pi. \tag{7.1}$$

The diffraction angle introduced by this simple DOE is directly transferred to a lateral repositioning of the optical trap from the centre position. Furthermore, we can use a quadratic phase distribution, the holographic equivalent of a refractive lens, of the kind $\phi(x, y) = \Gamma(x^2 + y^2) \mod 2\pi$ (Miyamoto 1961) in order to influence the divergence of the diffracted light (cf. Fig. 7.1b). The combination of both finally gives full three-dimensional control on the position of a single trap (cf. Fig. 7.1c):

$$\phi(x, y) = \left(\frac{2\pi}{\Lambda_x}x + \frac{2\pi}{\Lambda_y}y + \Gamma(x^2 + y^2) \right) \quad \mathrm{mod}\ 2\pi. \tag{7.2}$$

The full potential of DOEs, however, can be realised when considering the complex superposition of multiple gratings and holographic lenses (Liesener et al. 2000). Figure 7.1d shows an example where four traps at different three-dimensional positions are generated by a DOE that is calculated as the argument of the complex sum of four phase distributions calculated from Eq. (7.2). Effectively, this means it is not only possible to control the position of one single trap, but the laser beam can be split in a multitude of traps, each of which can be controlled independently from the others.

This analytical *gratings and lenses* approach to generate DOEs for multiple beams in HOT grants an intuitive understanding of the basic physics involved in the diffractive element. The most important advantage, however, is the relatively low computational expense, which enables fast calculation of holograms in real-time. Besides these advantages, the analytic calculation of holograms has several practical and conceptional drawbacks. The most prominent limitations are strong possible ghost traps (Polin et al. 2005; Hesseling et al. 2011), i.e. additional intensity peaks at undesired positions that are dictated by symmetry conditions. Furthermore, possible inhomogeneities of the individual optical traps (Curtis et al. 2005) and the limitation to discrete spots in contrast to extended, continuous optical landscapes are possible drawbacks of the analytic approach. Much effort has been invested in finding solutions for the suppression of ghost traps. In principle, one can reduce the symmetry of the trapping pattern by changing the positions of a few or all the traps (Curtis et al. 2005). This approach, however, is not universal as usually the trapping pattern cannot be changed without the loss of functionality. By randomly changing the phase of all traps, ghost traps can be reduced to some extent without changing the trapping pattern (Curtis et al. 2005). Another approach that is very successful in suppressing ghost traps is the *random mask encoding* method (Montes-Usategui et al. 2006; Mas et al. 2011). Here, diffraction gratings and lenses are randomly distributed to small sub-areas across the area of the DOE. Unfortunately, this approach significantly reduces diffraction efficiency and cannot be used for more than a small number of traps with reasonable power (Montes-Usategui et al. 2006).

7.1.2 Iterative Calculation of Holograms

An alternative approach for calculating holograms is the use of iterative Fourier transformation algorithms (IFTAs) (Fienup 1982). Therefore, we recall that the light field distribution in the focal plane of the microscope objective can be described as the Fourier transform of the light field at the back focal plane of the objective. In HOT the DOE and the back aperture of the objective are usually positioned in conjugate planes and thus the DOE and the intensity distribution in the trapping plane are also related by a Fourier transformation. If one wants to calculate the DOE corresponding to an arbitrary intensity distribution in the focal plane by calculating the Fourier transform, however, the result in general is a complex valued light field, structured in amplitude and phase. This is not feasible in most situations for two reasons. First, all available dynamic spatial light modulators can only modulate either amplitude or phase and not both (Zwick et al. 2010), and second, the modulation of the amplitude means an unavoidable loss of light intensity at the DOE and thus poor efficiency.

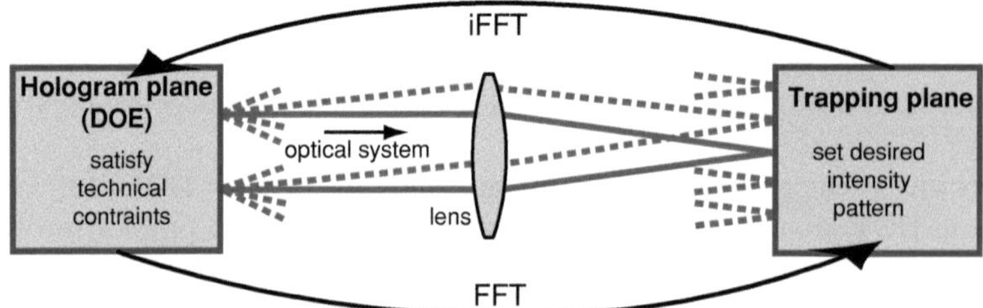

Fig. 7.2 Sketch of the basic function of IFTAs. The hologram plane and the trapping plane of the optical tweezers are connected by an optical Fourier transformation through the microscope objective. Numerically, fast Fourier transformations (*FFTs*) are used to propagate the light field iteratively between both planes and include physical constraints

The task to solve is finding a phase-only hologram or DOE that generates the desired intensity distribution and thus configuration of optical traps in the focal plane of the microscope objective. This problem in general cannot be solved analytically, but an iterative algorithm as sketched in Fig. 7.2 is usually applied (Gerchberg and Saxton 1972). The basic idea is to iterate numerically between the hologram (DOE) plane and the trapping plane. In the hologram plane, the technical constraints like the requirement for pure phase modulation, plane wave or TEM_{00} illumination, discretisation of phase values, or pixellation of the SLM are included. In the trapping plane, the intensity is always set to or approached to the desired intensity distribution. The algorithm can converge to a hologram only if there are enough degrees of freedom that can be chosen as required in every iteration step. Usually, the phase in the trapping plane is not of interest and can serve as a free parameter. Furthermore, the intensity in the periphery of the field of view is often of minor interest only and can be an additional free parameter (Zwick et al. 2010). The algorithm can be terminated when a suitable convergence criterion is fulfilled, like a certain number of iterations or when the deviation of the calculated pattern from the desired pattern is below a threshold.

The clear advantage of IFTAs is their flexibility and the quality of the resulting holograms. It is furthermore straightforward to extend the algorithms to three-dimensional intensity patterns in the trapping plane (Haist et al. 1997). Also, special constraints such as suppression of ghost traps or optimised homogeneity can be included elegantly (Hesseling et al. 2011). The versatility comes at the cost of a relatively high computational expense, limiting possible real-time applications. For the results discussed in this chapter, thus the analytic approach was utilised.

7.1.3 Experimental Implementation

HOT require a laser that is modulated by a DOE, relayed appropriately and focused through a high numerical aperture lens. Commonly, HOT are integrated into an optical microscope in order to facilitate simultaneous observation with standard microscope techniques, including bright field imaging, dark field imaging, phase-contrast imaging,[1] and fluorescence microscopy.

Within the framework of this thesis, two HOT setups have been designed and implemented. A custom-made setup was realised for maximal flexibility and access to all parts of the beam path. It relies on a $P_{max} = 2.0$ W frequency doubled Nd:YAG laser emitting at $\lambda = 532$ nm and an optically addressed "X8267-16" phase-only SLM from Hamamatsu Photonics with 768 x 768 pixels and a phase shift of up to 3.5π. The second implementation is based on a commercial microscope and optimised for biological experiments. In the following, general design considerations are discussed using the example of the second setup.

Figure 7.3 shows a sketch of the setup. The microscope can be easily identified. It consists of an illumination, a condenser, a translation stage that holds the sample, the microscope objective (MO), a tube lens (L_T) and a video camera. An inverted layout of the microscope—as in this implementation—is favourable for many biological samples, but not required for HOT in general. The depicted microscope also includes optional fluorescence illumination, which is integrated by means of a dichroic mirror DM_2. Conveniently, the MO used for microscopic investigations at the optical resolution limit is required to have a high numerical aperture. It is therefore possible to reuse the objective from the microscope to focus the laser light field with the required high numerical aperture.

The HOT part of the experimental setup basically consists of a laser, suitable relay optics, a phase-only SLM and the microscope objective. As the trapping laser, a $P_{max} = 2.5$ W continuous wave Nd : YVO$_4$ laser emitting at $\lambda = 1,064$ nm is used. Using near infrared light minimises photodamage to biological samples compared to wavelengths in the visible regime (Neuman et al. 1999). The required laser power depends strongly on the application scenario. Although stable optical trapping of 1 μm particles with less than 200 μW is possible with a perfectly corrected system (Cizmar et al. 2010), a more practical value—especially if a particle is to be moved fast—is a few milliwatts per particle. The laser beam is expanded and collimated in order to illuminate the active area of the SLM ("PLUTO", Holoeye Photonics, 1920 x 1080 pixels, 2π maximal phase shift), which acts as the DOE. Like the other phase-only SLMs employed for the experiments presented in this thesis, the PLUTO SLM can introduce 256 different phase level and it can be safely assumed that effects due to phase quantisation can be neglected (Goodman and Silvestri 1970). After the light field is structured by the SLM, it is relayed and imaged onto the back focal plane of the microscope objective. The illumination beam path and the laser beam path are separated by means of a dichroic mirror (DM_1).

---

[1] Phase-contrast imaging implies a phase-retarding element positioned in the zeroth diffraction order in a Fourier plane with respect to the sample plane. With standard research microscopes with phase-contrast mode this element is usually integrated into the microscope objectives. For optical tweezers a phase object in the microscope objective usually is not desired as it produces unintended changes of the tailored wave front. Still, simultaneous use of optical tweezers and phase-contrast imaging is possible with the phase retarding element positioned in an external Fourier plane as is, for example, offered by Nikon under the name *External Phase Contrast*.

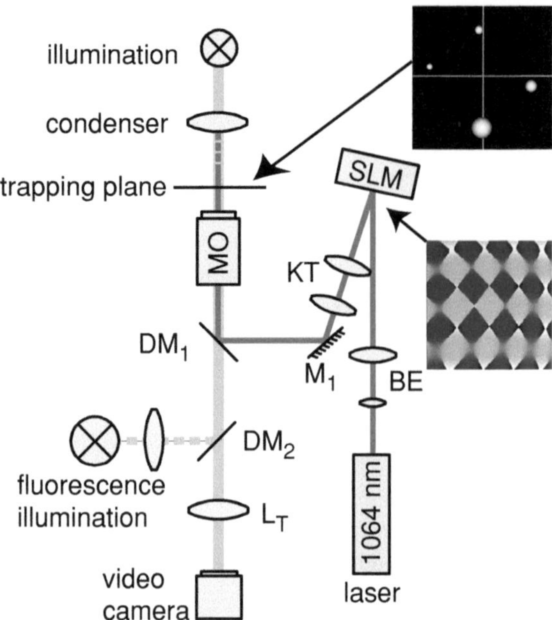

Fig. 7.3 Experimental implementation of holographic optical tweezers. *MO* microscope objective; L_T tube lens; DM_1 DM_2 dichroic mirrors, M_1 relay mirror; *KT* telescope; *BE* beam expansion. From (Woerdemann et al. 2012)

The optical traps generated with the implemented system can generate an optical potential well with a stiffness per input power of $k/mW = (2.1 \pm 0.2)(pN/\mu m)/mW$. The calibration was obtained for a $1\,\mu m$ polystyrene sphere, suspended in water ($n_{med} = 1.33$), using Eq. (2.16). Furthermore, a maximal force of $(0.155 \pm 0.005)pN/mW$ can be exerted on a $1\,\mu m$ polystyrene particle in a medium with refractive index $n_{med} = 1.36$ before it escapes the trap. This calibration was performed by moving the translation stage of the microscope with increasing velocities until the particle escaped. The refractive index of the medium was set by a mixture of 19% glycerol in water.

7.2 Applications of Holographic Optical Tweezers

One obvious though powerful application of HOT is the parallel execution of many experiments each of which it is possible to realise with single optical tweezers. An example could be the parallel measurement of forces on multiple cells in a biological assay. This enables processing studies that require a large number of statistically uncorrelated measurements rapidly and efficiently. Of particular interest, however, are scenarios that cannot be realised with single optical tweezers. For example, in order to measure the binding force of two microscopic objects it might be necessary to approach both objects and then separate them in a defined way.

Colloidal suspensions, i.e. particles suspended in a fluid, are a perfect field of activity for optical tweezers (Grier 1997). Single or double optical tweezers have been used to measure electrostatic (Crocker and Grier 1994) or hydrodynamic (Crocker 1997; Meiners and Quake 1999; Reichert and Stark 2004) interactions between two spherical particles. Optical tweezers can aid here in two ways. First, the absolute position of the particles under test with respect to other particles and surfaces can be defined and their relative position can be controlled precisely (Crocker and Grier 1994; Crocker 1997). Second, the optical trapping potential can be used directly to measure interaction forces (Meiners and Quake 1999; Reichert and Stark 2004). As soon as interactions between more than a very limited number of particles are involved it is not reasonable to use a discrete combination of single optical tweezers but HOT are preferable.

Even the early works with HOT demonstrate that multiple spherical particles can be trapped simultaneously at different three-dimensional positions (Liesener et al. 2000). Soon it was shown that even large arrays of colloidal spheres can be created with the holographic technique (Korda et al. 2002). These demonstrations were restricted to static configurations as they employed prefabricated, static DOEs.

The utilisation of computer controlled SLMs enabled the creation of complex, three-dimensional structures of multiple particles that can be dynamically rearranged (Curtis et al. 2002). Although there are competing concepts for dynamic three-dimensional control of multiple particles as, for example, a combination of time-shared traps for transversal positioning and an additional SLM for axial positioning (Melville et al. 2003), HOT have been established as first choice for many applications.

One important field is the assembly of three-dimensional crystalline (Sinclair et al. 2004) and quasicrystalline (Roichman and Grier 2005) structures with HOT. In Fig. 7.4, a basic example of a three-dimensional crystalline structure is shown that demonstrates the most important aspects. For this purpose, a suspension of polystyrene beads with a diameter of $1\,\mu m$ was prepared in demineralised water. Eight arbitrarily selected beads were trapped with HOT and arranged in the three-dimensional configuration in Fig. 7.4a. The three-dimensional positioning can be done interactively as the analytic approach is utilised to calculate the holograms, which is fast enough for real-time control (Leach et al. 2006). The structure in Fig. 7.4a corresponds to a simple cubic unit cell with roughly equal edge lengths. While the position of each bead can be chosen rather freely, the range of maximum possible transversal and axial displacements is limited to several tens of micrometers, depending on the resolution of the employed SLM (Sinclair et al. 2004). In the further sequence of Fig. 7.4 the unit cell is resized dynamically and then rotated as a whole. The high degree of control is basically attributed to the software that keeps track of the relative particle positions and calculates the appropriate holograms following the user input.

By this means even highly demanding structures of tens and hundreds of individual particles can be arranged and dynamically rearranged as required. This does not only allow for a deeper understanding of particle-particle interactions beyond the experimental nearest neighbour approximation, but also enables the creation of

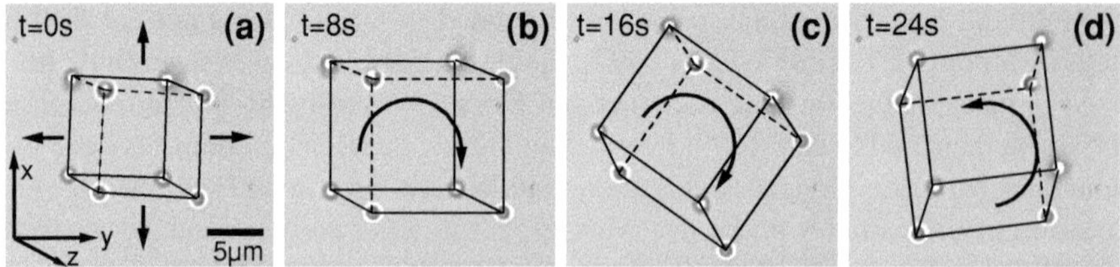

Fig. 7.4 Eight 1 µm polysterene beads, arranged in a simple cubic unit cell which is resized and rotated as a whole. The particle positions are connected with lines that visualise the geometric configuration. From (Woerdemann et al. 2012)

structures dedicated for a particular purpose. One exciting example is the creation of photonic band gap materials with HOT (Benito et al. 2008). The main advantage over competing techniques like photo-lithography, two-photon polymerisation, holography, or self-assembly of colloids is that the material is built with control on every single unit. By this means it is straightforward to introduce defects, including other materials, which is essential for tailoring the band gap structure (Braun et al. 2006).

7.3 Manipulation of Rod-Shaped Bacteria

Many exciting applications require a high degree of control on micro- and nanoparticles that are not spherical but feature arbitrary shapes. In the following, two important examples are discussed. The first is the class of bacteria, which, from the physical point of view, can be seen as dielectric and often non-spherical microscopic objects with a broad range of applications from the synthesis of substances (Rosenberg and Ron 1999), as active components of bio-hybrid systems (Sokolov et al. 2010), or for microfluidic lab-on-a-chip applications like mixing processes (Kim and Breuer 2007). In particular rod-shaped, self-propelled bacteria that achieve motility by rotational motion of their helical flagella filaments are of topical interest because they feature one of the smallest known rotational motors, a "nanotechnological marvel" (Berg 2003), and because their motion is well adapted to constraints of movements at low Reynolds numbers (Purcell 1977). The latter gives rise to a multitude of possible microfluidic applications, but also curiosity about the fundamental principles is a strong motivating force towards a deeper understanding of bacterial interaction (Cisneros et al. 2007), interaction with the microscopic environment (Darnton et al. 2004), or the formation behaviour of biofilms (Kolter and Greenberg 2006).

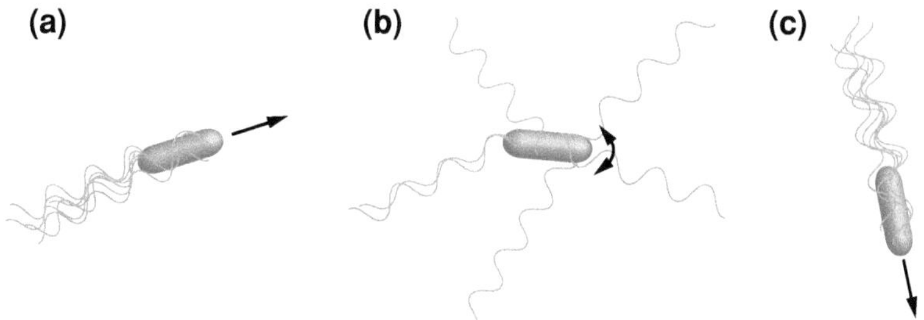

Fig. 7.5 Chemotactic strategy of flagellated bacteria like *B. subtilis* or *E. coli*. When all flagella rotate counter-clockwise they can bundle and enable the bacterium to swim efficiently (**a**). With a certain probability – which gets lower when the concentration of an attractant increases or the concentration of a repellent decreases – one or more flagella ocassionally rotate in clockwise direction, causing the flagella to unbundle (**b**). This induces a random re-orientation by means of tumbling of the bacterium before it starts swimming again (**c**)

7.3.1 *Bacillus Subtilis: A Model Bacterial Cell*

The model rod-shaped bacterium used for this experimental study is *Bacillus subtilis*, a widespread Gram-positive, non-pathogen bacterium with typical diameters of 1 μm and lengths of $2-3\,\mu$m. It features a number of helical filaments, the *flagella*, that are attached to the bacterial cell by means of rotary motor complexes (Ito et al. 2005). *B. subtilis* is peritrichously flagellated meaning that the flagella are arranged over the whole cell (Wolgemuth 2008). Each flagellum can be set into rapid rotation by the associated motor, either in clockwise (cw) or counter-clockwise (ccw) direction. Due to the symmetry breaking handiness of the helical flagella, the flagella can form a bundle if they rotate in one direction (ccw) but they un-bundle when they rotate in the other direction (cw) (Kim et al. 2003). This behaviour is essential for *chemotaxis*, a simple but effective algorithm of the bacteria that enables them to approach chemoattractants, in particular nutrients. When the flagella are bundled, the bacterium moves forward on a fairly straight trajectory, a state called *swimming* as illustrated in Fig. 7.5a. With a certain probability one or more flagella occasionally— typically every few seconds (Min et al. 2009)—change their direction of rotation and cause unbundling of the flagella bundle, resulting in a *tumbling* state of the cell (cf. Fig. 7.5b). During the tumbling, the bacterium reorients itself and afterwards starts with the directed motion again. For chemotaxis, the bacterium increases the probability of tumbling and decreases the probability of swimming when it senses a negative gradient of nutrient concentration, i.e. when it moves away from a food source. When the nutrient gradient on the other hand is positive, the bacterium will more likely keep on swimming in this direction and tumble less often. By obeying this simple rule, the bacterium will eventually reach the point of highest nutrition concentration.

All experiments described in the following were performed with wild type strain BD 630. The bacterial samples were defrosted, centrifuged at 9,000 rpm for

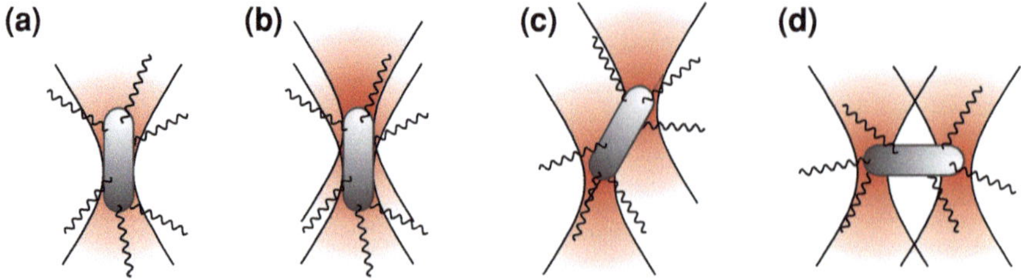

Fig. 7.6 Basic principle of full three-dimensional control over bacteria. Two optical traps can rotate the bacterial cell from its original orientation (**a**) into, for example, horizontal orientation (**d**)

2–3 min and resuspended in chemotaxis buffer (Ordal and Goldman 1975) at room temperature. Motility of the majority of these bacteria was visually confirmed before each experiment.

7.3.2 Full Three-Dimensional Position and Orientation Control

Optical tweezers are ideal tools to confine bacterial cells (Ashkin et al. 1987, Ashkin and Dziedzic 1987) and thus can be the starting point for a thorough analysis of hydrodynamic parameters, mutual interaction, or cooperative effects. However, like all elongated objects, rod-shaped bacteria always align their long axis with the axis of the focused laser beam (cf. Fig. 7.6a), resulting in a strong limitation of possible (lateral) observation and interaction scenarios (Simpson and Hanna 2011). Defined control of orientation would allow, for example, detailed studies on bacterial motility (Min et al. 2009). The strong demand for three-dimensional orientation control has led to a number of methods that extend the basic concept of optical tweezers, including support by a surface (Paterson et al. 2001; Moh et al. 2005), Hermite-Gaussian modes (Sato et al. 1991), linetraps (O'Neil and Padgett 2002; Dasgupta et al. 2003), oscillating traps (Carmon and Feingold 2011), Mathieu beams (Alpmann 2010), or multiple beam traps (Min et al. 2009; Agarwal et al. 2005; Gibson et al. 2008). For the complete and utter control over the three-dimensional position and, at the same time, over two or even all three rotational degrees of freedom, usually two or three single traps are utilised that can be steered individually to some extent (Bingelyte et al. 2003; Tanaka et al. 2007; Tanaka et al. 2008). Most of these approaches for complete control of rod-shaped bacteria, however, are restricted to one single bacterium or a very low quantity because they have strong requirements with respect to the mechanical or optical system, including the timing of mechanically operating components (Tanaka et al. 2007; Tanaka et al. 2008), or a direct correlation between quantity of desired traps and complexity of the setup (Min et al. 2009; Tanaka et al. 2007).

Thus, for the active alignment of elongated bacterial cells the ability of HOT to create an almost arbitrary number of individual optical traps is of crucial value. Figure 7.6 shows the basic principle of orientation control over rod-shaped bacteria,

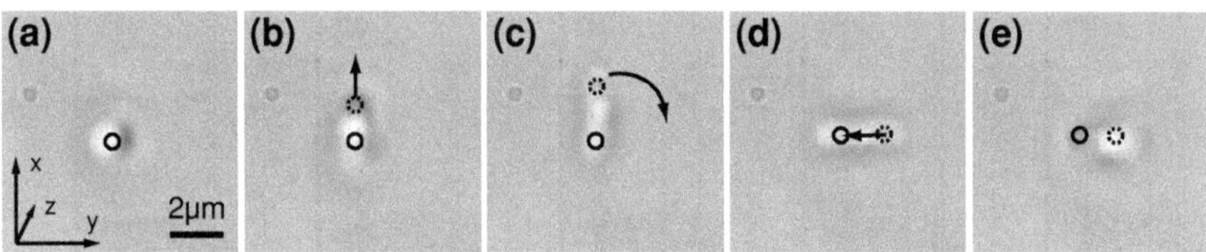

Fig. 7.7 Demonstration of full three-dimensional control over a rod-shaped bacterial cell. Initially, the cell's major axis is aligned with the beam axis (z-axis) of a single trap (*black circle*). An additional second trap (*dashed circle*) creates an optical potential that effects the re-orientation of the cell into a new position with an arbitrary angle $-90° \leq \alpha \leq 90°$ between observation ($x - y$) plane and the bacterial cell's major axis (**b**). The bacterium is brought into horizontal orientation ($\alpha = 0°$) (**c**) and rotated in the observation plane (**c**), (**d**). Finally, the bacterium again is rotated out of the horizontal orientation

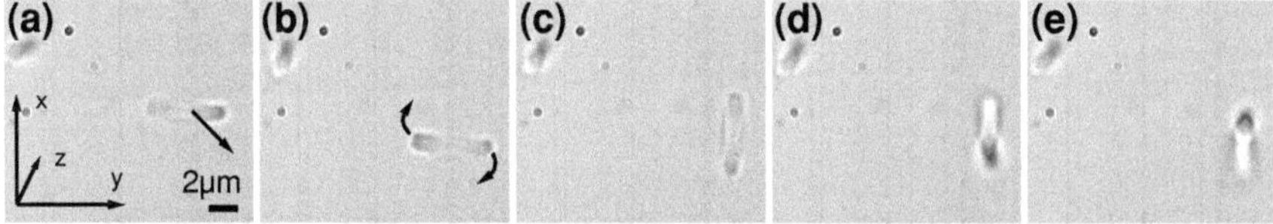

Fig. 7.8 Demonstration of control over orientation and position of a duplicating bacterial cell (length of approximately $6\,\mu$m). Translation (**a**) and orientation (**b**), (**c**) of the cell in the observation plane. The angle introduced between observation plane and bacterial cell is $\alpha = (35 \pm 5)°$ (**d**) and angle $\alpha = (27 \pm 5)°$ (**e**), respectively

B. subtilis in this example. First, the bacterial cell is confined in a single trap, aligned with the beam axis. A second trap is generated with HOT and placed in the vicinity of the first trap. The second trap is translated along an appropriately chosen trajectory so that the geometric distance between both laser foci is kept constant and approximately equals the length of the cell. By this means, both traps exert force on the poles of the cell and induce the exact amount of torque required for defined alignment. Any arbitrary angle α between the bacterium's long axis and the beam axis can be achieved including horizontal positioning of the cell (Fig. 7.6d). During the whole process the bacterial cell is trapped three-dimensionally, i.e. not supported by any surface, and with the available software both traps can be moved while preserving their relative positions and thus the orientation of the cell (Bingelyte et al. 2003; Hörner et al. 2010). Figure 7.7 shows the experimental results for a single bacterium with an aspect ratio (width:length) of approximately 1:2.5.

Even strongly elongated cells that cannot be handled with the simple two-trap approach can be controlled with HOT (Agarwal et al. 2005). Figure 7.8 shows a long bacterial cell, or more precisely a bacterial chain just before cell division, with a length of approximately $6\,\mu$m and an aspect ratio of approximately 1:6. In order to achieve full orientation control four individual traps in a linear configuration were used (Hörner et al. 2010).

Although the alignment of a single cell itself is of highest relevance (Min et al. 2009), the full strengths of HOT are revealed when the handling of multiple

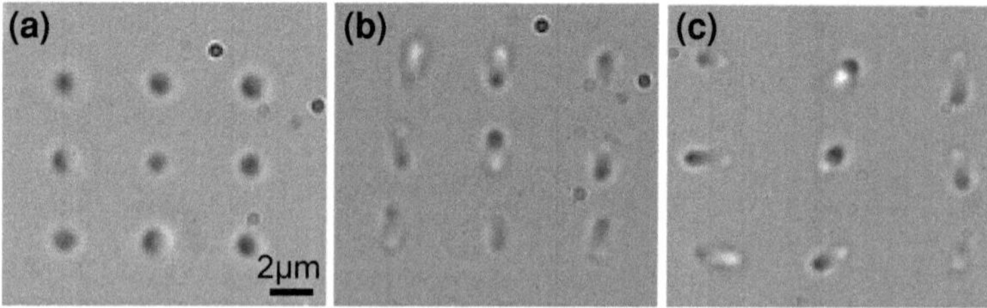

Fig. 7.9 Array of 3 x 3 *B. subtilis*, arranged with HOT. Each bacterial cell is controlled individually, leading to a configuration of bacteria that are aligned with the beam axis (**a**), a configuration of bacteria that are aligned parallel with each other and in lateral orientation (**b**), and a configuration that demonstrates different orientations of the bacteria in one assembly (**c**). From (Hörner et al. 2010)

bacteria is required. It is possible not only to have full orientation and translation control over one single bacterial cell but over a multitude of bacteria simultaneously with independent control on any individual cell. By this means, tens of bacteria can be positioned and arbitrarily aligned, providing ideal initial situations for complex interaction scenarios or massively parallel investigations (Hörner et al. 2010). Figure 7.9a shows an example of 3 x 3 *B. subtilis*, arranged in an array. Initially, all bacteria are aligned with the beam axis since each cell is held by one optical trap. In order to align the bacterial cells, for each initial trap one additional trap is created next to it. The traps are controlled in such a way that all bacteria are oriented in horizontal position and in parallel with each other (Fig. 7.9b). For the configuration shown in Fig. 7.9c the individual bacteria were aligned with defined angles with respect to the observation plane and with respect to the optical axis. This clearly demonstrates that each cell can be controlled individually with a high degree of flexibility. All cells are trapped three-dimensionally during the whole alignment procedure and can be moved through the sample volume at any time without losing their relative orientations.

In order to further demonstrate that the control of multiple bacteria is not restricted to simple arrays, another assembly of six bacteria has been realised. As shown in Fig. 7.10a, all the bacteria are arranged on a circle with a diameter of a few bacterial lengths. In alternating sequence, the bacteria are either horizontally aligned or aligned to have an angle $\alpha \approx 45°$ with the beam axis. The configuration is dynamically rearranged into a circle of six horizontally aligned bacteria. This particular arrangement, for example, could be useful to create confined flow scenarios or complex scattering scenarios which allow detailed bottom-up studies of the formation of structures within bacterial suspensions (Aranson et al. 2007; Gyrya et al. 2010).[2]

---

[2] The experiments discussed in this section were performed in collaboration with Mr Florian Hörner within the framework of his diploma thesis (Hörner 2010) and have resulted in a joint publication (Hörner et al. 2010).

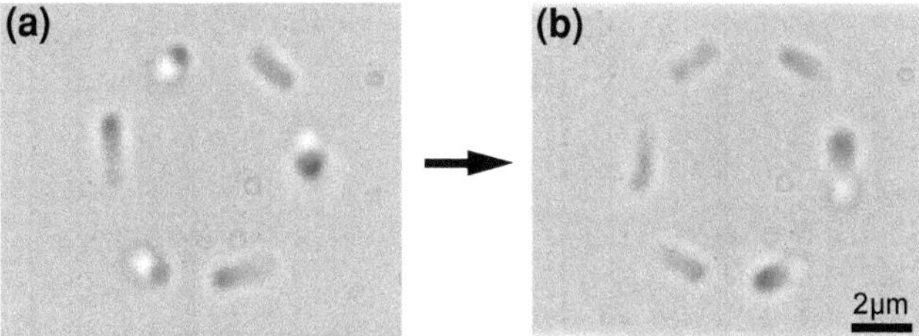

Fig. 7.10 Six *B. subtilis*, arranged in two different circular configurations. From (Hörner et al. 2010)

7.4 Managing Organisation of Microporous Molecular Hosts

HOT are well suited to confine, manipulate, and arrange microscopic and nanoscopic container particles. Within the framework of this thesis, a scheme has been developed for one particularly promising application, the optical assembly and organisation of nanocontainers that host specific guest molecules which themselves are highly ordered inside the containers (Woerdemann et al. 2010a, b, c). The synthesis of molecular structures and materials that are held together by non-covalent interactions, commonly named *supramolecular organisation*, can be one way towards the design of novel, functional materials with tailored properties that exploit the strong relationship between molecular arrangements and resulting macroscopic properties (Elemans et al. 2003). In particular, the hierarchical organisation of pre-ordered structures is a promising approach to bridge different ordering scales – from the molecular up to the macroscopic level (Woerdemann et al. 2010b).

7.4.1 Zeolite L: A Model Host Material for Supramolecular Organisation

Microporous molecular sieves like zeolite crystals are well-suited host materials for supramolecular organisation as they feature pores or cavities whose high geometric order directly transfers to a high degree of order of the guest molecules (Bruhwiler and Calzaferri 2004). This first level of organisation is relatively well accessible by chemical means (Calzaferri et al. 2011). The further organisation of the host particles is usually accessed by means of self-organisation or pre-patterned surfaces. While these approaches can be very efficient for large-scale arrangements, they provide only very limited control over the individual hosts (Ruiz et al. 2006).

HOT, on the other hand, are perfectly adapted to the precise control of a finite number of particles. In the following, zeolite L crystals are chosen to demonstrate *hierarchical* supramolecular organisation induced by HOT. Zeolite L are crystalline aluminosilicates with a cylindrical shape that feature strictly parallel nanochannels,

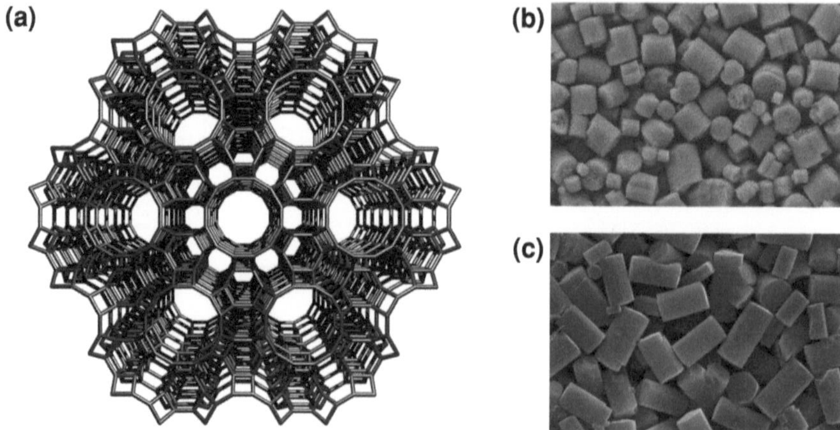

Fig. 7.11 Zeolite L crystals. **a** Sketch of the framework, revealing the inner structure with parallel nanochannels. **b, c** SEM images of the used zeolite samples. The smaller zeolites (**b**) have a nominal size of 1 μm × 1 μm (diameter x length); the longer zeolites (**c**) have a nominal size of 1 μm × 3 μm. It can be seen that the zeolites are not perfectly monodisperse

arranged in a hexagonal structure and running parallel to the cylinder axis (Bruhwiler and Calzaferri 2004). The channels have a diameter of 0.7 nm at the entrances, a maximum diameter of 1.3 nm and a channel to channel distance of 1.8 nm (Busby et al. 2008). Zeolite L crystals are versatile hosts and can be loaded with a wide range of inorganic and organic guest molecules including many dyes (Megelski and Calzaferri 2001). Zeolite L are transparent in the visible wavelength regime and their refractive index is approximately $n_{\mathrm{zeo}} = 1.49$ (Busby et al. 2008).

For the experiments described in the following, two different zeolite L samples were used. First, short zeolites with a diameter of roughly 1 μm and a similar height (cf. Fig. 7.11b) and second, clearly elongated zeolites with a diameter of about 1 μm and a height of about 3 μm (cf. Fig. 7.11c). Most experiments were performed with empty, i.e. not loaded, zeolites or zeolites loaded with DXP (N, N'-bis(2,6-dimethyl phenyl)-3,4:9,10-perylentetracarboxylic diimide) (El-Daly 1999) dye. For a few demonstrations, other loadings were used, in particular oxonine (Ox) and pyronine (Py). Usually, the samples were suspended in demineralised water or, for a few demonstrations, in the organic solvent acetonitrile (CH_3CN).

7.4.2 Optical Control of Zeolite L

The first important result is the observation that both the short (1 μm) and the long (3 μm) zeolite crystals can be trapped with optical tweezers when they are not loaded. The clearly elongated zeolites always align their long axis with the laser beam axis, analogous to the bacterial cells with a similar aspect ratio. The 1 μm zeolites in

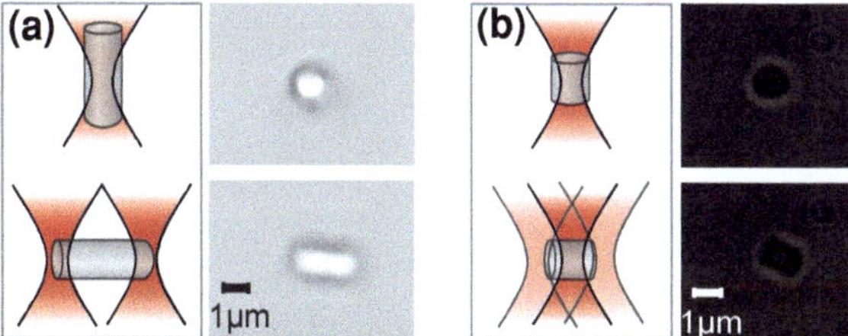

Fig. 7.12 Position and orientation control of zeolite L crystals. **a** Clearly elongated crystals are rotated with two single tweezers. **b** Zeolite L crystals with an aspect ratio close to one require a more sophisticated approach with multiple tweezers of different relative strength. From (Woerdemann et al. 2010a)

most of the observed cases also align their cylinder axis with the beam axis although exceptions are possible. For the vision of hierarchical supramolecular assemblies, it is important that not only empty but also loaded crystals can be manipulated. Therefore, empty zeolites and zeolites loaded with DXP dye are investigated with respect to their trapping properties in near-infrared ($\lambda = 1,064$ nm) and green ($\lambda = 532$ nm) laser light. DXP is a fluorescence dye that is strongly excited at $\lambda = 532$ nm (El-Daly 1999). It turns out that empty zeolites can be trapped with either wavelength, reflecting their high transparency at these wavelengths. The dye-loaded crystals, however, behave differently. While there was no difference found between empty and dye-loaded crystals at the infrared wavelength, the loaded particles avoid the laser focus of the green light rather than being trapped by it. Thus, they act as absorbing particles and are repelled from regions of high light intensity by means of the scattering force that is exerted on them during absorption (Woerdemann et al. 2010a). From this example it can be concluded that loaded particles can be trapped with optical tweezers if the loading shows no significant absorption at the trapping wavelength.

For the most versatile degree of control it is desirable to have additionally full orientation control over each individual zeolite particle. With the longer zeolite L crystals it is relatively easy to achieve orientation control with two or more traps in a linear configuration as shown in Fig. 7.12a. Crystals of a length close to their diameter, however, require a more sophisticated approach due to their small asymmetry. With an optimised viscosity[3] of the solvent and a tailored trapping configuration consisting of a strong central trap, which defines the position of the crystal, and two weaker side traps, which induce the rotation, it is possible to rotate these crystals into horizontal orientation (Woerdemann et al. 2010a) (cf. Fig. 7.12b).

Having in mind that complex assemblies of zeolites are desired, it is beneficial to have a reservoir, i.e. a place with high particle density, where particles can be picked up in order to assemble them at another location without unintentionally interfering particles. With the wavelength-selective absorbance properties of dye-

---

[3] The viscosity was increased by a factor of 6.0 compared to pure water, using a mixture of 50 % water and 50 % glycerol (Segur and Oberstar 1951).

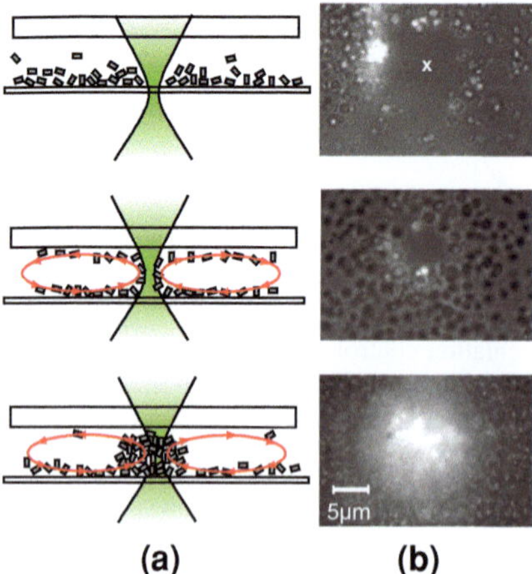

(a)   (b)

Fig. 7.13 Gradients of particle density induced by HOT. **a** Sketch of the experimental configuration as a side view. The laser focus is first positioned at the cover slip, where the (absorbing) particles avoid the laser beam (*top*). An adhered particle can serve as the initial heat source and induce strong convection roles (*middle*). When the laser focus is positioned slightly inside the sample volume, the process can become self-amplified and transport large numbers of particles towards the vicinity of the focus (*bottom*). **b** Experimental transverse microscope images corresponding to the respective situation. The approximate position of the laser focus is marked with "x" in the top image. From (Woerdemann et al. 2010a)

loaded zeolites, one particularly elegant method for the generation of the necessary gradient of particle density is available. When dye-loaded zeolites are brought close to the optical trap that operates at an excitation wavelength of the dye, they usually are repelled by the laser focus (cf. Fig. 7.13a). However, there are usually a few particles that adhere to the walls of the sample cell. In this case, the particle strongly absorbs energy and acts as a strong local heat source. In a typical sample geometry as indicated in the figure, i. e. a small sample volume between an object slide and a cover slip and gravity acting along the laser beam axis, the local heat source can induce convection rolls. These convection rolls transport large numbers of particles within a few seconds that accumulate in the vicinity of the laser focus. This results in a relatively small area with a very high particle density, surrounded by an area with low particle density. From the reservoir, particles can be picked up conveniently with an optical trap operating at a different wavelength where the dye is not absorbing.

7.4.3 Hierarchical Supramolecular Organisation

Figure 7.14a shows an example of 4 x 4 zeolite L crystals arranged in a rectangular Bravais lattice configuration. All the crystals are trapped simultaneously with HOT and their relative and absolute three-dimensional position is exactly defined by the

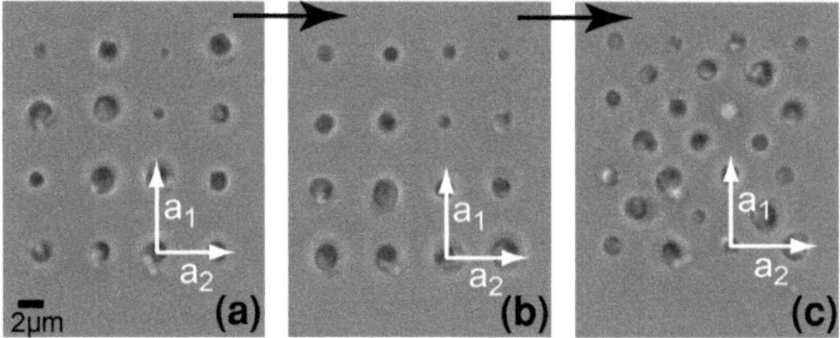

Fig. 7.14 Dynamic patterning of cylindrical zeolite L crystals with nominal dimensions of 1 µm. The crystals are organised in a rectangular Bravais lattice configuration (**a**), ordered by their size (**b**) and reconfigured dynamically in a centred rectangular lattice (**c**). From (Woerdemann et al. 2012)

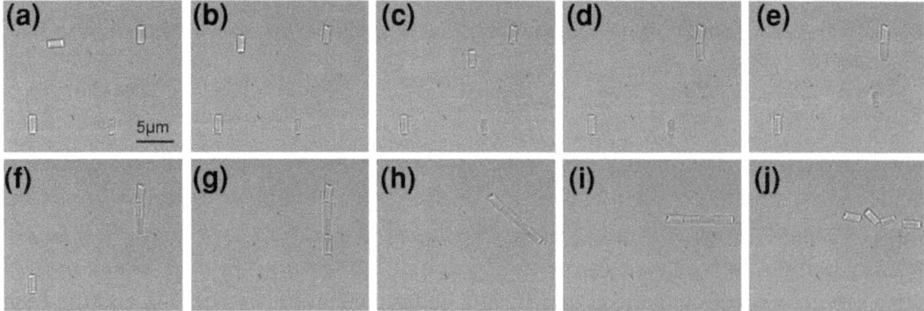

Fig. 7.15 "On the fly" assembly of 3 µm zeolite L. Four crystals are aligned and assembled (**a**)–(**g**) into a linear configuration which subsequently is rotated (**h**), (**i**) and disintegrated (**j**)

laser light field. The whole structure can be easily translated in x, y, or z-direction without being disturbed. It is obvious that this high degree of control is not possible with classical manipulation methods or with chemical means. Furthermore, it is possible to increase the degree of organisation dynamically, for example, by ordering the crystals in the array by their size (Fig. 7.14b). Finally, Fig. 7.14c shows that the lattice can be reconfigured into a centred rectangular lattice. For this purpose, additional zeolites are taken from a reservoir and added to the structure at the geometrically relevant positions. This is done interactively and in real-time, and the configuration is given by the user, not by any constraints of the method.

The ability of interactive handling is further demonstrated in Fig. 7.15, where four elongated zeolites, held in lateral orientation by two optical tweezers each, are individually moved and positioned. First, they are aligned with their long axes (Fig. 7.15a, b) and subsequently assembled to a linear configuration (Fig. 7.15c–g). The assembly is only held by optical forces and can be rotated as a whole by means of appropriate trajectories of the eight optical traps (Fig. 7.15g–i). When the laser is turned off, the particles diffuse (Fig. 7.15j), clearly showing that they did not physically adhere to each other.

The high degree of control over individual container particles that HOT provide in tandem with their ability to control tens or even hundreds of particles is a promis-

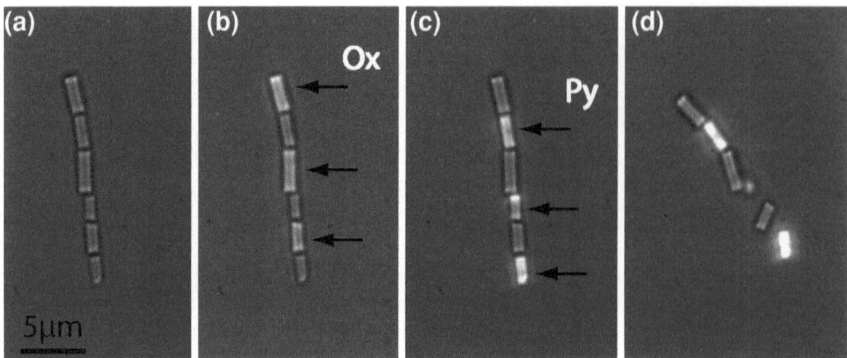

Fig. 7.16 Linear assembly of six differently loaded zeolite crystals, arranged in alternating configuration

ing approach for designing novel materials with exciting properties that cannot be achieved by conventional means. One simple but conclusive example of a functional assembly is shown in Fig.7.16. For this configuration, two differently loaded zeolite samples were used; one with Py-dye and one with Ox-dye. Seven crystals were selectively trapped and arranged in a linear configuration with alternating loading. The fluorescence signal of the dyes is monitored under appropriate illumination, enabling, e.g., highly localised generation of different structured microscopic light patterns.

7.5 Conclusion and Perspectives

Optical manipulation with HOT is a well established technique. The vast majority of applications so far, however, has been restricted to spherical particles or sphere-like biological cells. In this chapter, we have reviewed a few important concepts of HOT and discussed a number of exciting applications. The versatility that makes HOT ideal tools for the handling of complexly shaped microscopic objects was utilised to handle two different kinds of non-spherical objects.

Many bacteria are elongated biological cells that cannot be oriented with conventional optical tweezers. With HOT is has been shown that these cells can be rotated and positioned at will, enabling, for example, microscopic investigations that were not possible before. Furthermore, elaborated assemblies of multiple bacteria can be designed to enable in-depth studies on mutual interactions, e.g. induced by hydrodynamic flows that are generated by their actively rotating flagella filaments.

Zeolite L is a model microporous nanocontainer that can host a multitude of different, functional, loadings. In this chapter, the necessary techniques have been developed that enable free positioning and orientation control of single container particles – in contrast to established, chemical methods that are restricted to the control of larger ensembles and lack any fine control. It has been shown that even loaded particles can be trapped with HOT. If the loading is a fluorescence dye, the particles exhibit exciting properties when interacting with light of different wavelengths. By appropriate choices of the trapping laser wavelengths, dye-loaded particles can act as either transparent or absorbing particles. It has been demonstrated that a multitude of empty or loaded containers can be arranged in highly ordered assemblies. These organised structures can reveal exciting properties that can be tailored by the choice of loadings and the geometric configuration.

References

Agarwal R, Ladavac K, Roichman Y, Yu G, Lieber C, Grier D (2005) Manipulation and assembly of nanowires with holographic optical traps. Opt Express 13:8906–8912

Alpmann C (2010) Maßgeschneiderte Lichtfelder zur mehrdimensionalen Manipulation von Materie in optischen Pinzetten. Master's thesis, Westfälische Wilhelms-Universität Münster

Aranson I, Sokolov A, Kessler J, Goldstein R (2007) Model for dynamical coherence in thin films of self-propelled microorganisms. Phys Rev E 75:040901

Ashkin A, Dziedzic J (1987) Optical trapping and manipulation of viruses and bacteria. Science 235:1517–1520

Ashkin A, Dziedzic J, Yamane T (1987) Optical trapping and manipulation of single cells using infrared laser beams. Nature 330:769–771

Benito D, Carberry D, Simpson S, Gibson G, Padgett M, Rarity J, Miles M, Hanna S (2008) Constructing 3D crystal templates for photonic band gap materials using holographic optical tweezers. Opt Express 16:13005–13015

Berg H (2003) The rotary motor of bacterial flagella. Annu Rev Biochem 72:19–54

Bingelyte V, Leach J, Courtial J, Padgett M (2003) Optically controlled three-dimensional rotation of microscopic objects. Appl Phys Lett 82:829–831

Braun P, Rinne S, Garcia-Santamaria F (2006) Introducing defects in 3D photonic crystals: State of the art. Adv Mater 18:2665–2678

Bruhwiler D, Calzaferri G (2004) Molecular sieves as host materials for supramolecular organization. Micropor Mesopor Mater 72:1–23

Busby M, Blum C, Tibben M, Fibikar S, Calzaferri G, Subramaniam V, De Cola L (2008) Time, space, and spectrally resolved studies on J-aggregate interactions in zeolite L nanochannels. J Am Chem Soc 130:10970–10976

Calzaferri G, Meallet-Renault R, Bruhwiler D, Pansu R, Dolamic I, Dienel T, Adler P, Li H, Kunzmann A (2011) Designing dye-nanochannel antenna hybrid materials for light harvesting, transport and trapping. ChemPhysChem 12:580–594

Carmon G, Feingold M (2011) Rotation of single bacterial cells relative to the optical axis using optical tweezers. Opt Lett 36:40–42

Cisneros L, Cortez R, Dombrowski C, Goldstein R, Kessler J (2007) Fluid dynamics of self-propelled microorganisms, from individuals to concentrated populations. Exp Fluids 43:737–753

Cizmar T, Mazilu M, Dholakia K (2010) In situ wavefront correction and its application to micromanipulation. Nat Photonics 4:388–394

Crocker J (1997) Measurement of the hydrodynamic corrections to the Brownian motion of two colloidal spheres. J Chem Phys 106:2837–2840

Crocker J, Grier D (1994) Microscopic measurement of the pair interaction potential of charge-stabilized colloid. Phys Rev Lett 73:352–355

Curtis J, Koss B, Grier D (2002) Dynamic holographic optical tweezers. Opt Commun 207:169–175

Curtis J, Schmitz C, Spatz J (2005) Symmetry dependence of holograms for optical trapping. Opt Lett 30:2086–2088

Darnton N, Turner L, Breuer K, Berg H (2004) Moving fluid with bacterial carpets. Biophys J 86:1863–1870

Dasgupta R, Mohanty S, Gupta P (2003) Controlled rotation of biological microscopic objects using optical line tweezers. Biotechnol Lett 25:1625–1628

El-Daly S (1999) Spectral, lifetime, fluorescence quenching, energy transfer and photodecomposition of N, N'-bis(2,6-dimethyl phenyl)-3,4:9,10-perylentetracarboxylic diimide (DXP). Spectrochim Acta, Part A 55:143–152

Elemans J, Rowan A, Nolte R (2003) Mastering molecular matter. Supramolecular architectures by hierarchical self-assembly. J Mater Chem 13:2661–2670

Fienup J (1982) Phase retrieval algorithms—a comparison. Appl Opt 21:2758–2769

Gerchberg R, Saxton W (1972) A practical algorithm for determination of phase from image and diffraction plane pictures. Optik 35:237–246

Gibson G, Carberry D, Whyte G, Leach J, Courtial J, Jackson J, Robert D, Miles M, Padgett M (2008) Holographic assembly workstation for optical manipulation. Appl Phys B-Lasers O 10:044009

Goodman J, Silvestri A (1970) Some effects of Fourier-domain phase quantization. IBM J Res Dev 14:478

Grier D (1997) Optical tweezers in colloid and interface science. Curr Opin Colloid In 2:264–270

Gyrya V, Aranson I, Berlyand L, Karpeev D (2010) A model of hydrodynamic interaction between swimming bacteria. Bull Math Biol 72:148–183

Haist T, Schönleber M, Tiziani H (1997) Computer-generated holograms from 3D-objects written on twisted-nematic liquid crystal displays. Opt Commun 140:299–308

Hesseling C, Woerdemann M, Hermerschmidt A, Denz C (2011) Controlling ghost traps in holographic optical tweezers. Opt Lett 36:3657–3659

Hörner F (2010) Dreidimensionale, optisch induzierte Manipulation von Mikropartikeln. Master's thesis, Westfälische Wilhelms-Universität Münster

Hörner F, Woerdemann M, Müller S, Maier B, Denz C (2010) Full 3D translational and rotational optical control of multiple rod-shaped bacteria. J Biophoton 3:468–475

Ito M, Terahara N, Fujinami S, Krulwich T (2005) Properties of motility in Bacillus subtilis powered by the H+-coupled MotAB flagellar stator, Na+-coupled MotPS or hybrid stators MotAS or MotPB. J Mol Biol 352:396–408

Kim M, Breuer K (2007) Controlled mixing in microfluidic systems using bacterial chemotaxis. Anal Chem 79:955–959

Kim M, Bird J, van Parys A, Breuer K, Powers T (2003) A macroscopic scale model of bacterial flagellar bundeling. Proc Natl. Acad Sci U.S.A. 100:15485

Kolter R, Greenberg E (2006) Microbial sciences—the superficial life of microbes. Nature 441:300–302

Korda P, Spalding G, Dufresne E, Grier D (2002) Nanofabrication with holographic optical tweezers. Rev Sci Instrum 73:1956–1957

Leach J, Wulff K, Sinclair G, Jordan P, Courtial J, Thomson L, Gibson G, Karunwi K, Cooper J, Laczik ZJ, Padgett M (2006) Interactive approach to optical tweezers control. Appl Opt 45:897–903

Liesener J, Reicherter M, Haist T, Tiziani H (2000) Multi-functional optical tweezers using computer-generated holograms. Opt Commun 185:77–82

Mas J, Roth M, Martin-Badosa E, Montes-Usategui M (2011) Adding functionalities to precomputed holograms with random mask multiplexing in holographic optical tweezers. Appl Opt 50:1417–1424

Megelski S, Calzaferri G (2001) Tuning the size and shape of zeolite L-based inorganic-organic host-guest composites for optical antenna systems. Adv Funct Mater 11:277–286

Meiners J, Quake S (1999) Direct measurement of hydrodynamic cross correlations between two particles in an external potential. Phys Rev Lett 82:2211–2214

Melville H, Milne G, Spalding G, Sibbett W, Dholakia K, McGloin D (2003) Optical trapping of three-dimensional structures using dynamic holograms. Opt Express 11:3562–3567

Min T, Mears P, Chubiz L, Rao C, Golding I, Chemla Y (2009) High-resolution, long-term characterization of bacterial motility using optical tweezers. Nat Methods 6:831–835

Miyamoto K (1961) The phase Fresnel lens. J Opt Soc Am 51:17–20

Moh K, Lee W, Cheong W, Yuan X (2005) Multiple optical line traps using a single phase-only rectangular ridge. Appl Phys B 80:973–976

Montes-Usategui M, Pleguezuelos E, Andilla J, Martin-Badosa E (2006) Fast generation of holographic optical tweezers by random mask encoding of Fourier components. Opt Express 14:2101–2107

Neuman K, Chadd E, Liou G, Bergman K, Block S (1999) Characterization of photodamage to Escherichia coli in optical traps. Biophys J 77:2856–2863

O'Neil A, Padgett M (2002) Rotational control within optical tweezers by use of a rotating aperture. Opt Lett 27:743–745

Ordal G, Goldman D (1975) Chemotaxis away from uncouplers of oxidative phosphorylation in Bacillus subtilis. Science 189:802–805

Paterson L, MacDonald M, Arlt J, Sibbett W, Bryant P, Dholakia K (2001) Controlled rotation of optically trapped microscopic particles. Science 292:912–914

Polin M, Ladavac K, Lee S, Roichman Y, Grier D (2005) Optimized holographic optical traps. Opt Express 13:5831–5845

Purcell E (1977) Life at low reynolds-number. Am J Phys 45:3–11

Reichert M, Stark H (2004) Hydrodynamic coupling of two rotating spheres trapped in harmonic potentials. Phys Rev E: Stat Nonlinear Soft Matter Phys 69:031407

Roichman Y, Grier D (2005) Holographic assembly of quasicrystalline photonic heterostructures. Opt Express 13:5434–5439

Rosenberg E, Ron E (1999) High- and low-molecular-mass microbial surfactants. Appl Microbiol Biot 52:154–162

Ruiz A, Li H, Calzaferri G (2006) Organizing supramolecular functional dye-zeolite crystals. Angew Chem Int Ed 45:5282–5287

Sato S, Ishigure M, Inaba H (1991) Optical trapping and rotational manipulation of microscopic particles and biological cells using higher-order mode Nd-YAG laser-beams. Electron Lett 27:1831–1832

Segur J, Oberstar H (1951) Viscosity of glycerol and its aqueous solutions. Ind Eng Chem 43:2117–2120

Simpson SH, Hanna S (2011) Optical trapping of microrods: variation with size and refractive index. J Opt Soc Am A 28:850–858

Sinclair G, Jordan P, Courtial J, Padgett M, Cooper J, Laczik Z (2004) Assembly of 3-dimensional structures using programmable holographic optical tweezers. Opt Express 12:5475–5480

Sinclair G, Jordan P, Leach J, Padgett M, Cooper J (2004) Defining the trapping limits of holographical optical tweezers. J Mod Opt 51:409–414

Sokolov A, Apodaca M, Grzybowski B, Aranson I (2010) Swimming bacteria power microscopic gears. Proc Natl Acad Sci U.S.A. 107:969–974

Tanaka Y, Hirano K, Nagata H, Ishikawa M (2007) Real-time three-dimensional orientation control of non-spherical micro objects using laser trapping. Electron Lett 43:412–414

Tanaka Y, Kawada H, Hirano K, Ishikawa M, Kitajima H (2008) Automated manipulation of non-spherical micro-objects using optical tweezers combined with image processing techniques. Opt Express 16:15115–15122

Woerdemann M, Gläsener S, Hörner F, Devaux A, De Cola L, Denz C (2010a) Dynamic and reversible organization of zeolite L crystals induced by holographic optical tweezers. Adv Mater 22:4176–4179

Woerdemann M, Alpmann C, Hoerner F, Devaux A, De Cola L, Denz C (2010b) Optical control and dynamic patterning of zeolites. SPIE Proc 7762:77622E

Woerdemann M, Devaux A, De Cola L, Denz C (2010c) Managing hierarchical supramolecular organization with holographic optical tweezers. OPN (Optics in 2010) 21:40
Woerdemann M, Alpmann C, Denz C (2012) Optical imaging and metrology, chapter three-dimensional particle control by holographic optical tweezers. Wiley-VCH Verlag, Weinheim
Wolgemuth C (2008) Collective swimming and the dynamics of bacterial turbulence. Biophys J 95:1564–1574
Zwick S, Haist T, Warber M, Osten W (2010) Dynamic holography using pixelated light modulators. Appl Opt 49:F47–F58

Chapter 8
Summary and Outlook

The manipulation of matter on a microscopic scale solely by means of light has dramatically gained in importance during the last decade. In particular light fields that are structured either in space or in time or both have a high potential with respect to novel applications. While the "classical" field of optical tweezers uses one of the simplest kinds of optical light fields, i.e. a stationary focused Gaussian beam, more complex light fields can increase the versatility and utility of optical micromanipulation significantly. The work presented in this thesis has identified several novel concepts that will help developing optical micromanipulation further towards application driven needs.

With the concept of holographic phase contrast a method has been developed that tackles many problems usually associated with the generation of multiple optical traps by means of a spatial light modulator. While Fourier-plane approaches can be computationally expensive and can be subject to undesired effects like ghost traps or non-uniform distribution of intensity to individual traps, holographic phase contrast avoids these issues by utilising an image plane for the structuring of the light field. The necessary transfer of the phase distribution to a structured intensity pattern is performed by means of (volume) holographic interferometry in a photorefractive holographic material. It has been shown that the proposed configuration is indeed capable of generating the intensity distributions desired for advanced optical trapping applications. Besides single and multiple traps, also more complex, e.g. ring shaped or hierarchically ordered, structures can be achieved without any additional effort. Although the employed holographic material, photorefractive lithium niobate, was well suited for the investigation of the fundamental properties of the system, future research initially should intensively study available alternatives with emphasis on write-once-read-many polymer materials or photorefractive materials where the volatility can be switched as required.

Another ubiquitous limitation of conventional optical tweezers is the high numerical aperture that is unavoidably required in unidirectional configurations and limits available working distances and implies high light intensities at the position of the optical trap. Within the framework of this thesis, a concept of counter-propagating

M. Woerdemann, *Structured Light Fields*, Springer Theses, 117
DOI: 10.1007/978-3-642-29323-8_8, © Springer-Verlag Berlin Heidelberg 2012

optical traps was investigated, where an additional, "back-propagating" light field is generated by means of optical phase conjugation. State-of-the-art applications often require advanced features, including multiple traps and the dynamic movement of individual traps. The basic concept of phase-conjugate counter-propagating optical traps has been developed towards a multifunctional system where almost arbitrarily structured light fields can be used. This includes arrays of intensity peaks which can trap according numbers of particles and higher order modes with interesting features like optical vortices. It has been demonstrated that even dynamically changing field distributions can be used in the phase-conjugate configuration. Although the inter-action of transient light fields with the dynamics of the phase-conjugating mirror can be somewhat complex, it has been successfully shown that particles cannot only be stably trapped but also moved at will. The system thus developed can serve as a universal platform for various optical micromanipulation experiments. For biolog-ical questions, however, the employed green wavelength is not optimal. The next research steps towards this important field of applications should thus focus on the infrared wavelength regime.

With non-diffracting beams, a class of light fields was introduced that can produce axially extended optical potential wells. While there are a few examples in literature where non-diffracting beams are used for optical micromanipulation, the majority of those is limited to relatively simple Bessel beams. With Mathieu beams, a new class of non-diffracting beams was identified that opens exciting perspectives in optical micromanipulation. First, they feature a wide range of transverse modes that can be selected according to the intended applications. Second, owing to their elliptical symmetry, their shape can be tuned by the ellipticity parameter. This enables tai-loring the symmetry of the optical potential well to the shape of the particles to be trapped and predestines Mathieu beams for the trapping of non-spherical particles. Two proof-of-principle experiments emphasising the particular features of Mathieu beams were developed. It has been shown that multiple, spherical particles can be trapped, piled up in axial direction. This is possible due to the axial extension of the light field, combined with its self-reconstructing properties. With the second experiment is has been shown that non-spherical, elongated particles align them-selves within the lateral intensity distribution of a Mathieu beam while, additionally, multiples of these particles were be stacked in axial direction. Mathieu beams are an analytical solution of the Helmholtz equation in elliptical coordinates. There is, however, an infinite number of different light fields that are given by the Whittaker integral. In order to exploit the beneficial properties of general non-diffracting beams in optical micromanipulation experiments, it would be advantageous to develop a multi-purpose platform that can generate all possible non-diffracting beams and apply them to optical micromanipulation.

Quite in contrast to non-diffracting beams, self-similar beams like the Ince-Gauss-ian beams do change their transverse intensity distribution during propagation. This change, however, happens in a way that the beam always has exactly the same structure except for a (known) scaling factor. The propagation properties enable the efficient holographic generation of Ince-Gaussian beams in any optical plane, including the Fourier plane. Ince-Gaussian beams are well suited to produce highly structured intensity distributions that can be selected from a wide range of different modes. In this thesis it has been successfully shown that the three-dimensional optical potential landscapes induced by appropriately processed Ince-Gaussian beams can be used to transfer the high degree of order of the light modes to accordingly organised microparticles. The here presented experiments should form the starting point towards an extensive use of Ince-Gaussian beams for the creation of highly sophisticated micro-structures that potentially have most exciting applications.

Holographic optical tweezers, although they can have many disadvantages, which have been addressed in the discussed concepts, certainly have in favour their high degree of versatility. Within the framework of this thesis, two new applications of holographic optical tweezers have been developed. First, it has been shown that non-spherical bacterial cells can be positioned and oriented at will with appropriately structured holographic optical tweezers. Furthermore, complex arrangements of multiple cells can be created with full position and orientation control on every individual cell. By these means, highly defined exploratory interaction scenarios of different numbers of individuals can be prepared which can be the onset for in-depth studies of bacterial interaction. The second application of holographic optical tweezers that was investigated is defined arrangements of particular nano-containers. By means of the example of zeolite L, it has been shown that non-spherical nanocontainers can be well handled with optical tweezers, even when they are loaded with functional molecules. A whole set of tools has been developed in order to be able to create complex, three-dimensional assemblies of zeolite L with a varying degree of order. Finally, hierarchical supramolecular organisation was demonstrated, induced by holographic optical tweezers.

Appendix A
Encoding Amplitude Information
on Phase-Only Diffractive Optical Elements

When light fields are shaped holographically with DOEs, usually only amplitude or phase can be specified rather than the full complex wavefront because typical modulators cannot encode the complex amplitude $\hat{U} = |\hat{U}|e^{i\Psi}$ directly. In particular, it is often preferred to utilise phase-only modulators because they offer superior diffraction efficiency and hence utilisation of the available light. For many applications, the (real) amplitude information can be neglected. This, for example, is successfully done in HOT when only the argument of the complex superposition of multiple gratings and holographic lenses [cf. Eq. (7.2)] is taken into account while the amplitude is discarded. For the generation of advanced light fields with high fidelity, however, complex modulation is essential. For example, the mode purity of holographically generated LG beams [cf. Eq. (2.17)] is limited to approximately 0.85 when generated with phase-only DOEs (Ando et al. 2009). There are a couple of methods available that enable additional encoding of (real) amplitude information on phase-only DOEs (Kirk and Jones 1971; Davis et al. 1999; Kettunen et al. 1997; Davis et al. 2003; Arrizón et al. 2009), yielding—in this example—a mode purity very close to one (Ando et al. 2009).

The basic idea of encoding amplitude information on a phase-only modulator is simple. In general, a high frequency carrier grating is utilised that redistributes light between different orders of diffraction, resulting in locally varying intensities corresponding to $|\hat{U}|$ in one order. For example, we assume a desired amplitude and phase distribution as depicted in Fig. A.1a and b, respectively. The carrier signal in this example is a blazed diffraction grating (Fig. A.1c) that efficiently diffracts light into the +1st order of diffraction. When the contrast of the diffraction grating is reduced, i.e. it has a modulation of less than 2π, diffraction efficiency is also reduced and the light which is not diffracted into the +1st order remains in the 0th order. The concept thus is to reduce the diffraction efficiency in those areas of the DOE where the desired amplitude is low while maintaining the diffraction efficiency where high amplitude levels are desired as illustrated in Fig. A.1d. This modulated diffraction grating yields the desired amplitude distribution in the +1st order of diffraction. The desired phase distribution can be simply added to the

M. Woerdemann, *Structured Light Fields*, Springer Theses,
DOI: 10.1007/978-3-642-29323-8, © Springer-Verlag Berlin Heidelberg 2012

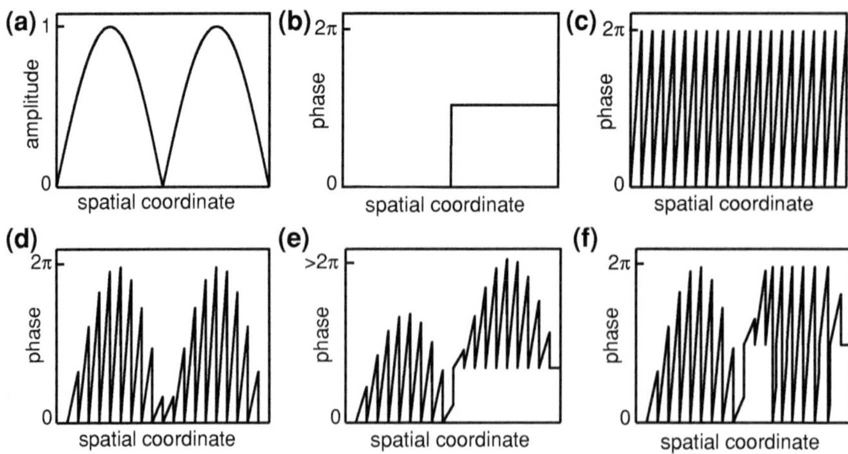

Fig. A.1 Basic principle of encoding complex amplitudes on phase-only DOEs. **a** and **b** show a sample (real) amplitude and a sample phase, respectively. The blazed grating in (**c**) reflects all light into the +1st order of diffraction. When the contrast of the blazed grating is locally modulated, so is the diffraction efficiency. By this means, the amplitude information is encoded on the blazed grating (**d**). The desired phase distribution can be be added (**e**) and the result, if necessary modulo 2π (**f**) will produce a wave front with the desired complex amplitude distribution in the +1st order

grating (cf. Fig. A.1e), resulting in a diffracting element that effectively modulates both, the amplitude and the phase of a light wave. Since typical phase modulators are only capable of introducing a phase retardation of one wavelength, i.e. $(0\ldots2\pi)$ radians, the phase shift to be applied can be wrapped accordingly if necessary (cf. Fig. A.1f).

The illustrated encoding method for the realisation of complex valued transmission or reflection functions can be understood in terms of a Fourier series representation, assuming that the complex function $U(u)\exp(i\Psi(u))$ is supposed to be encoded for the spatial coordinate u. One concrete implementation for the encoding of this complex function on phase-only modulators is the choice of a phase distribution (Davis et al. 1999)

$$\Phi(u) = \exp(iU(u)\Psi(u)), \tag{A.1}$$

i.e. a multiplication of the amplitude and the phase. This phase distribution can be represented by a Fourier series as (Davis et al. 1999)

$$\Phi(u) = \sum_{n=-\infty}^{\infty} \Phi_n(u)\exp(in\Psi(u)), \tag{A.2}$$

with the coefficients

$$\Phi_n(u) = \exp(i(n - U(u))\pi)\frac{\sin(\pi(n - U(u)))}{\pi(n - U(u))}. \tag{A.3}$$

For the first diffraction order, $m = 1$, the phase term in $\Phi(u)$ reproduces the desired phase $\Psi(u)$ and the coefficient $\Phi_n(u)$ approximates the desired amplitude $U(u)$ (Davis et al. 1999). The phase term in Eq. (A.3) and the sinc function introduce errors in the reproduced amplitude. These can be compensated by using a distorted amplitude $U'(u)$ that can be calculated from the desired $U(u)$ for a given order of, say $n = 1$ here, such that it annuls the distortions introduced by the nonlinear relation in Eq. (A.3) (Davis et al. 1999). In order to spatially separate the different orders of diffraction, a linear phase term is added to the phase distribution, i.e. $\Psi(u) \rightarrow \Psi(u) + \frac{2\pi}{\Lambda}u$. This introduces, after wrapping the phases, an underlying blazed grating with the period Λ which spatially separates the desired image from the 0th order of diffraction. Alternatively, a quadratic phase could be added that separates the different diffraction orders along the beam axis (cf. Sect. 7.1.1).

There are various different approaches to encode complex modulation on a phase-only modulator. They differ in the choice of the carrier signal (Kirk and Jones 1971; Arrizón et al. 2009), in the choice of the encoding function (Eq. (A.1)) (Ando et al. 2009; Arrizón et al. 2007), and in the employed order of diffraction (Arrizón et al. 2009). Furthermore, the quantisation of the phase levels needs to be taken into account. While complex amplitude encoding can be an advantage even with two available phase levels (Davis et al. 2003), all modulators employed for the experiments described in this thesis were capable of applying $N = 256$ phase levels. Since the intensity of resulting noise is proportional to $1/N^2$, we can safely neglect additional errors introduced by the phase quantisation.

Appendix B
Mathematical Functions

B.1 Details on the Calculation of Mathieu Functions

The Mathieu Eq. (5.10) has even $(\mathrm{ce}_m(u,q))$ and odd $(\mathrm{se}_m(u,q))$ solutions (Whittaker 1912; Arscott 1964). The solutions are dependent on the parity of the order m so that we expect four equations:

$$\mathrm{ce}_{2n}(\eta,q) = \sum_{r=0}^{\infty} A_{2r}(q) \cos(2r\eta) \tag{B.1}$$

$$\mathrm{ce}_{2n+1}(\eta,q) = \sum_{r=0}^{\infty} A_{2r+1}(q) \cos((2r+1)\eta) \tag{B.2}$$

$$\mathrm{se}_{2n+1}(\eta,q) = \sum_{r=0}^{\infty} B_{2r+1}(q) \sin((2r+1)\eta) \tag{B.3}$$

$$\mathrm{se}_{2n+2}(\eta,q) = \sum_{r=0}^{\infty} B_{2r+2}(q) \sin((2r+2)\eta), \tag{B.4}$$

with $n = 0, 1, 2, \ldots$ The expansion coefficients A_i, B_i of this Fourier series can be obtained as elements of the eigenvectors A, B of the Mathieu equation (Gutierrez-Vega et al. 2003).

While the ordinary Mathieu functions $\mathrm{ce}_m(u,q)$ and $\mathrm{se}_m(u,q)$ can be directly identified as the solutions of the angular Mathieu equation, solutions of the radial Mathieu equation are obtained with the substitution $\eta = \mathrm{i}\xi$. Hence, the modified Mathieu functions are given as:

$$\mathrm{Je}_{2n}(\xi,q) = \mathrm{ce}_{2n}(\mathrm{i}\xi,q) = \sum_{r=0}^{\infty} A_{2r}(q) \cosh(2r\xi) \tag{B.5}$$

M. Woerdemann, *Structured Light Fields*, Springer Theses,
DOI: 10.1007/978-3-642-29323-8, © Springer-Verlag Berlin Heidelberg 2012

$$\text{Je}_{2n+1}(\xi, q) = \text{ce}_{2n+1}(i\xi, q) = \sum_{r=0}^{\infty} A_{2r+1}(q) \cosh((2r+1)\xi) \qquad (\text{B.6})$$

$$\text{Jo}_{2n+1}(\xi, q) = \text{se}_{2n+1}(i\xi, q) = \sum_{r=0}^{\infty} B_{2r+1}(q) \sinh((2r+1)\xi) \qquad (\text{B.7})$$

$$\text{Jo}_{2n+2}(\xi, q) = \text{se}_{2n+2}(i\xi, q) = \sum_{r=0}^{\infty} B_{2r+2}(q) \sinh((2r+2)\xi), \qquad (\text{B.8})$$

where $\text{Je}_m(\xi, q)$ and $\text{Jo}_m(\xi, q)$ are the even and odd modified Mathieu functions of order m.

The functions are calculated numerically in MATLAB,[1] following References (Stamnes and Spjelkavik 1995) and (Cojocaru 2008). For a given value of q there are four infinite sequences of eigenvalues a, corresponding to the respective four solutions. Substituting Eqs. (B.1–B.4) into the Mathieu Eq. (5.10) yields recurrence relations for the expansion coefficients A_i, B_i. These relations can be written in matrix form (Stamnes and Spjelkavik 1995) and the eigenvalue problem is solved in MATLAB (Cojocaru 2008). In order to limit the computational expense to a reasonable value, the number of expansion coefficients in Eqs. (B.1–B.4) and (B.5–B.8) is set to $r_{\max} = 25$, following convergence considerations (Cojocaru 2008).

B.2 Details on the Calculation of Ince Polynomials

The Ince Eq. (6.6) has even $(C_p^m(\eta, \epsilon))$ and odd $(S_p^m(\eta, \epsilon))$ solutions which additionally depend on the parity of degree m and order p.[2] In contrast to the Mathieu functions, the four solutions are finite sums and called Ince polynomials (Arscott 1964; Bandres and Gutierrez-Vega 2004):

$$C_{2n}^{2k}(\eta, \epsilon) = \sum_{r=0}^{n} A_r(\epsilon) \cos(2r\eta) \qquad k = 0, \ldots n \qquad (\text{B.9})$$

$$C_{2n+1}^{2k+1}(\eta, \epsilon) = \sum_{r=0}^{n} A_r(\epsilon) \cos((2r+1)\eta) \qquad k = 0, \ldots n \qquad (\text{B.10})$$

$$S_{2n}^{2k}(\eta, \epsilon) = \sum_{r=1}^{n} B_r(\epsilon) \sin(2r\eta) \qquad k = 1, \ldots n \qquad (\text{B.11})$$

---

[1] MathWorks MATLAB website–http://www.mathworks.de, Sept 2011.

[2] Recall that degree m and order p have the same parity.

$$S_{2n+1}^{2k+1}(\eta, \epsilon) = \sum_{r=0}^{n} B_r(\epsilon) \sin((2r+1)\eta) \qquad k = 0, \ldots n, \qquad (B.12)$$

with $n = 0, 1, 2, \ldots$ Analogous to the Mathieu solutions, the expansion coefficients A_r, B_r are obtained from an analysis of the eigenvalues a. Therefore, Eqs. (B.9–B.12) are substituted into the Ince Eq. (6.6), yielding recurrence relations for the coefficients. From these relations, finite tridiagonal matrices are constructed (Bandres and Gutierrez-Vega 2004) and the eigenvalue problem is solved numerically with MATLAB. For a given order p, a finite ensemble of eigenvalues is obtained. The elements of the eigenvector A or B corresponding to the mth eigenvalue in an ordered list can be identified as the expansion coefficients A_r or B_r, respectively (Bandres and Gutierrez-Vega 2004).

While these Ince polynomial $C_p^m(\eta, \epsilon)$ and $S_p^m(\eta, \epsilon)$ can be directly identified as the solutions of the ("angular") Ince Eq. (6.6), solutions of the "radial" Ince Eq. (6.5) are obtained with the substitution $\eta = i\xi$ (Bandres and Gutierrez-Vega 2004):

$$C_{2n}^{2k}(i\xi, \epsilon) = \sum_{r=0}^{n} A_r(\epsilon) \cosh(2r\xi) \qquad k = 0, \ldots n \qquad (B.13)$$

$$C_{2n+1}^{2k+1}(i\xi, \epsilon) = \sum_{r=0}^{n} A_r(\epsilon) \cosh((2r+1)\xi) \qquad k = 0, \ldots n \qquad (B.14)$$

$$S_{2n}^{2k}(i\xi, \epsilon) = \sum_{r=1}^{n} B_r(\epsilon) \sinh(2r\xi) \qquad k = 1, \ldots n \qquad (B.15)$$

$$S_{2n+1}^{2k+1}(i\xi, \epsilon) = \sum_{r=0}^{n} B_r(\epsilon) \sinh((2r+1)\xi) \qquad k = 0, \ldots n. \qquad (B.16)$$

References

Ando T, Ohtake Y, Matsumoto N, Inoue T, Fukuchi N (2009) Mode purities of Laguerre-Gaussian beams generated via complex-amplitude modulation using phase-only spatial light modulators. Opt Lett 34:34–36

Kirk J, Jones A (1971) Phase-only complex-valued spatial filter. J Opt Soc Am 61:1023–1028

Davis J, Cottrell D, Campos J, Yzuel M, Moreno I (1999) Encoding amplitude information onto phase-only filters. Appl Opt 38:5004–5013

Kettunen V, Vahimaa P, Turunen J, Noponen E (1997) Zeroth-order coding of complex amplitude in two dimensions. J Opt Soc Am A 14:808–815

Davis J, Valadez K, Cottrell D (2003) Encoding amplitude and phase information onto a binary phase-only spatial light modulator. Appl Opt 42:2003–2008

Arrizón V, Ruiz U, Mendez G, Apolinar-Iribe A (2009) Zero order synthetic hologram with a sinusoidalphase carrier for generation of multiple beams. Opt Express 17:2663–2669

Arrizón V, Ruiz U, Carrada R, González L (2007) Pixelated phase computer holograms for the accurate encoding of scalar complex fields. J Opt Soc Am A 24:3500–3507

Whittaker E (1912) In: Proceedings International Congress of Mathematicians, vol 1. Cambridge

Arscott F (1964) Periodic differential equations. Pergamon Press, Oxford

Gutierrez-Vega J, Rodriguez-Dagnino R, Meneses-Nava M, Chavez-Cerda S (2003) Mathieu functions, a visual approach. Am J Phys 71:233–242

Stamnes J, Spjelkavik B (1995) New method for computing eigenfunctions (Mathieu functions) for scattering by elliptical cylinders. Pure Appl Opt 4:251

Cojocaru E (2008) Mathieu functions computational toolbox implemented in Matlab. ArXiv e-prints, arXiv:0811.1970v2

Bandres M, Gutierrez-Vega J (2004) Ince-Gaussian modes of the paraxial wave equation and stable resonators. J Opt Soc Am A 21:873–880

M. Woerdemann, *Structured Light Fields*, Springer Theses,
DOI: 10.1007/978-3-642-29323-8, © Springer-Verlag Berlin Heidelberg 2012

Curriculum Vitae

Personal information

Name: Mike Woerdemann
Date of birth: 8th October 1980
Place of birth: Bad Laer
Nationality: German

School education

1987–1991   Primary school St. Ambrosius, Ostbevern
1991–2000   Collegium Johanneum, Ostbevern
     Degree: Abitur (general qualification for university entrance)

Compulsory military service

2000–2001   3 months of basic training, then 9 months in the HR department

University education

2001–2007   Westfälische Wilhelms Universität, Münster
     Course of studies: Physics
2003   Vordiplom (intermediate examination)
2004   Semester abroad in Sydney, Australia
2007   Degree: Diplom (Master's equivalant) in Applied Physics,
     Major: Nonlinear Photonics
2007–2011   Doctoral candidate, research group of Prof. Denz, Nonlinear Photonics
2011   Degree: Doctor of Science (Dr. rer. nat.)

Work experience

1995–1997   Ripploh Elektrotechnik GmbH, Ostbevern

M. Woerdemann, *Structured Light Fields*, Springer Theses,
DOI: 10.1007/978-3-642-29323-8, © Springer-Verlag Berlin Heidelberg 2012

1997–1998   Westeria Fördertechnik, Ostbevern
1998–2002   Aral Tankstelle, Ostbevern
2002–2005   zeb/information.technologie, Münster
2005–2007   Student assistant, research group of Prof. Denz
2007–2011   Research assistant, research group of Prof. Denz
since 2012   Postdoctoral research fellow, research group of Prof. Denz

Journal articles

- C. Alpmann, **M. Woerdemann**, and C. Denz, *Tailored light fields: a novel approach for creating complex optical traps*, Optics and Photonics News (Optics in 2011) **22**, 28 (2011)
- C. Hesseling, **M. Woerdemann**, A. Hermerschmidt, and C. Denz, *Controlling ghost traps in holographic optical tweezers*, Optics Letters **36**, 3657 (2011)
- **M. Woerdemann**, C. Alpmann, and C. Denz, *Optical assembly of microparticles into highly ordered structures using Ince-Gaussian beams*, Applied Physics Letters **98**, 111101 (2011)
- **M. Woerdemann**, A. Devaux, L. De Cola, and C. Denz, *Managing hierarchical supramolecular organization with holographic optical tweezers*, Optics and Photonics News (Optics in 2010) **21**, 40 (2010)
- C. Alpmann, **M. Woerdemann**, and C. Denz, *Mathieu beams as versatile light moulds for 3D micro particle assemblies*, Optics Express **18**, 26084 (2010)
- **M. Woerdemann**, K. Berghoff, and C. Denz, *Dynamic multiple-beam counter-propagating optical traps using optical phase-conjugation*, Optics Express **18**, 22348 (2010)
- **M. Wördemann**, C. Alpmann, F. Hörner, A. Devaux, L. De Cola, and C. Denz, *Optical control and dynamic patterning of zeolites*, Proceedings of SPIE **7762**, 77622E (2010)
- **M. Woerdemann**, S. Gläsener, F. Hörner, A. Devaux, L. De Cola, and C. Denz, *Dynamic and reversible organization of zeolite L crystals induced by holographic optical tweezers*, Advanced Materials **22**, 4176 (2010)
- M. Esseling, F. Holtmann, **M. Woerdemann**, and C. Denz, *Two-dimensional dielectrophoretic particle trapping in a hybrid crystal/PDMS-system*, Optics Express **18**, 17404 (2010)
- F. Hoerner, **M. Woerdemann**, S. Mueller , B. Maier, and C. Denz, *Full 3D translational and rotational optical control of multiple rod-shaped bacteria*, Journal of Biophotonics **3**, 468 (2010)
- **M. Woerdemann**, C. Alpmann, and C. Denz, *Self-pumped phase conjugation of light beams carrying orbital angular momentum*, Optics Express **17**, 22791 (2009)
- **M. Woerdemann**, C. Alpmann, and C. Denz, *Self-pumped phase conjugation of light beams carrying orbital angular momentum*, Photorefractive Materials, Effects and Devices: Control of Light and Matter, P2-28 (2009)
- M. Eßeling, F. Holtmann, M. Oevermann, **M. Wördemann**, and C. Denz, *Depth Resolution of Dynamic Phase-Contrast Microscopy*, Photorefractive Materials, Effects and Devices: Control of Light and Matter, T10-2 (2009)

- **M. Woerdemann**, F. Holtmann, and C. Denz, *Holographic phase contrast for dynamic multiple-beam optical tweezers*, Journal of Optics A: Pure and Applied Optics **11**, 034010 (2009)
- C. Denz, F. Holtmann, **M. Woerdemann**, and M. Oevermann, *Nonlinear dynamic phase contrast microscopy for microfluidic and microbiological applications*, Proceedings of SPIE **7038** (2008)
- **M. Woerdemann**, F. Holtmann, and C. Denz, *Full-field particle velocimetry with a photorefractive optical novelty filter*, Applied Physics Letters **93**, 021108 (2008)
- F. Holtmann, **M. Woerdemann**, J. Imbrock, and C. Denz, *Micro-fluidic velocimetry by photorefractive novelty filtering*, Controlling Light with Light—Photorefractive Effects, Photosensitivity, Fiber Gratings, Photonic Materials and More, SuD3 (2007)
- F. Holtmann, **M. Wördemann**, M. Oevermann, and C. Denz, *Optisch ver-stärkte Bewegungsdetektion zur zeitaufgelösten Geschwindigkeitsfeldvermessung in Mikroströmungen*, Proceedings of GALA, 54-1 (2007)
- F. Holtmann, V.V. Krishnamachari, O. Grothe, H. Deitmar, M. Eversloh, **M. Wördemann**, and C. Denz, *Measurement of density changes in fluid flow by an optical nonlinear filtering technique*, Proceedings of ISFV, 183-1 (2006)
- F. Holtmann, M. Eversloh, **M. Wördemann**, O. Grothe, H. Deitmar, V.V. Krishnamachari, and C. Denz, *Echtzeitbestimmung von Geschwindigkeits- und Dichtefeldern in Mikroströmungen mit Hilfe optisch nichtlinearer Bildaufnahme*, Proceedings of GALA, 49-1 (2006)

Book chapter

- **M. Woerdemann**, C. Alpmann, and C. Denz, *Three-dimensional particle control by holographic optical tweezers* in Optical Imaging and Metrology, Wiley-VCH Verlag, Weinheim (2012), to be published

Diplomarbeit (diploma thesis)

- **M. Wördemann**, *Optische Bewegungsdetektion als Instrument zur Geschwindigkeitsfeldanalyse in der Mikrofluidik.* Westfälische Wilhelms-Universität Münster (2007)

Selected conference contributions

- **M. Woerdemann**, C. Alpmann, M. Veiga Gutierrez, A. Devaux, L. De Cola, and C. Denz, *Holographic optical tweezers induced organization of structured nanocontainers*, 10th Mediterranean Workshop and Topical Meeting "Novel Optical Materials and Applications", Cetraro, Italy (2011)
- **M. Woerdemann**, C. Alpmann, A. Devaux, L. De Cola, and C. Denz, *Holographic optical tweezers induced hierarchical supramolecular organization*, The European Conference on Lasers and Electro-Optics (CLEO/Europe), Munich, Germany (2011)
- C. Alpmann, R. Bowman, **M. Woerdemann**, M. Padgett, and C. Denz, *Three-dimensional particle manipulation in stereoscopic optical tweezers using*

complex non-diffracting elliptical beams, Biophotonics—Advanced Trapping and Optofluidics in Life Sciences in the frame of the EOS Annual Meeting, Paris, France (2010)

- **M. Wördemann**, S. Gläsener, F. Hörner, A. Devaux, L. De Cola, and C. Denz, *Optical control and dynamic patterning of zeolites*, Optical Trapping and Optical Micromanipulation VII in the frame of SPIE Optics & Photonics, San Diego, USA (2010)
- F. Hörner, **M. Woerdemann**, S. Müller, B. Maier, and C. Denz, *3D translational and orientational optical control of multiple rod-shaped bacteria*, NanoBio-Europe, Münster, Germany (2010)
- **M. Woerdemann**, S. Gläsener, F. Hörner, A. Devaux, L. De Cola, and C. Denz, *Optical control and dynamic patterning of Zeolite L*, Nanophotonics in the frame of SPIE Europe, Brussels, Belgium (2010)
- **M. Woerdemann**, F. Hörner, S. Müller, B. Maier, and C. Denz, *Holographic optical tweezers aided investigation on Bacillus subtilis*, Photonics4Life Scientific Meeting, St Andrews, Scotland (2010)
- K. Berghoff, **M. Woerdemann**, and C. Denz, *Optische Doppel-Pinzette mit phasenkonjugierten Strahlen*, 111. Jahrestagung der DGaO, Wetzlar, Germany (2010)
- C. Denz, **M. Woerdemann**, S. Gläsener, F. Hörner, *Creating organization by light—optical control of microporous particles and molecular nanomotors by holographic optical tweezers*, Trends in Optical Micromanipulation II, Obergurgl, Austria (2010)
- **M. Woerdemann**, C. Alpmann, C. Denz, *Helical optical traps by phase conjugation of vortex beams*, Photonics4Life Scientific Meeting, Barcelona, Spain (2009)
- **M. Woerdemann**, C. Alpmann, and C. Denz, *Self-pumped phase conjugation of light beams carrying orbital angular momentum*, Photorefractive Materials, Effects, and Devices—Control of Light and Matter, Bad Honnef, Germany (2009)
- **M. Woerdemann**, F. Holtmann, and C. Denz, *Holographic phase contrast for dynamic multiple-beam optical tweezers*, Photonics4Life Scientific Meeting, Brussels, Belgium (2009)
- **M. Wördemann**, M. Oevermann, F. Holtmann, M. Eversloh, A. Hartmann, and C. Denz, *Flow Field Analysis with Dynamic Phase Contrast Microscopy and Optical Micromanipulation in Microfluidic Systems*, International Symposium on Scanning Probe Microscopy & Optical Tweezers in Life Sciences, Berlin, Germany (2009)